American Language Hub

LEVEL 5
Workbook with Key

+ access to Audio

macmillan education

Macmillan Education Limited
4 Crinan Street
London N1 9XW

Companies and representatives throughout the world

American Language Hub Level 5 with Key ISBN 978-1-786-32438-2
American Language Hub Level 5 with Key + access to Audio
ISBN 978-1-786-32436-8

Written by Signature Manuscripts

Signature Manuscripts has asserted their right to be identified as the author of this work in accordance with the Copyright, Designs and Patents Act 1988.

First published 2020

Original design by emc design ltd
Page make-up by SPi Global
Cover design based on original design by Restless
Cover photographs by plainpicture/Cavan Images, Getty Images/Luís Henrique Boucault
Picture research by Emily Taylor

The authors and publishers would like to thank the following for permission to reproduce their photographs:

Alamy p67, Alamy/Mackney p36(tl); **EyeEm**/Amit Goldstein p71(a); **Getty Images**/10'000 Hours p25, Getty Images/AFP/Philippe Huguen p15, Getty Images/Ty Allison p33, Getty Images/Apexphotos p14, Getty Images/Arterra p30(tl), Getty Images/AscentXmedia p35, Getty Images/Thomas Barwick pp5, 12, Getty Images/Benoitb p43(tr), Getty Images/Chris Bennett p56, Getty Images/Rimma Bondarenko p57(c), Getty Images/Sydney Bourne p29(tr), Getty Images/Bill Brooks p18(tl), Getty Images/Claudia Burlotti p4(tr), Getty Images/Caiaimage/Trevor Adeline p6, Getty Images/Caiaimage/Paul Bradbury p54, Getty Images/Caiaimage/Agnieszka Olek pp37, 41, Getty Images/Caiaimage/Chris Ryan p32, Getty Images/Cavan Images p34, Getty Images/Amos Chapple p39(tl), Getty Images/Tom Cockrem p23, Getty Images/Cultura p50, Getty Images/Cultura/Frank and Helena p61, Getty Images/Design Pics Inc p30(tr), Getty Images/EyeEm/Severin Matusek p36(br), Getty Images/Adam Gault p45, Getty Images/Geber86 p59, Getty Images/Georgijevic p26, Getty Images/Glow Wellness p29(tl), Getty Images/Mike Harrington p52(mr), Getty Images/Hero Images pp13, 42, 46(tr), Getty Images/Jon Hicks p71(c), Getty Images/Insights p43(tl), Getty Images/iStockphoto pp7, 46(tl), 48, Getty Images/Istetiana p57(d), Getty Images/Jacobs Stock Photography Ltd p64, Getty Images/Johner RF p46(b), Getty Images/Kanawa_Studio p68, Getty Images/Aleksi Koskinen p70, Getty Images/Justin Lambert p60, Getty Images/Justin Lewis p51, Getty Images/Roo Lewis p36(bl), Getty Images/Matthias Makarinus p40, Getty Images/Maremagnum p16, Getty Images/Nomad p4(br), Getty Images/OatmealStories p57(b), Getty Images/Seb Oliver p20, Getty Images/Kiszon Pascal pp63, 71(b), Getty Images/PeopleImages p55, Getty Images/PhotoDisc p58, Getty Images/Rawpixel p66(tr), Getty Images/Miguel Sanz p38, Getty Images/SolStock pp21, 69, Getty Images/TommL p53, Getty Images/Claudia Totir p57(a), Getty Images/David Aaron Troy p8, Getty Images/Universal Images Group p17, Getty Images/VCG p22, Getty Images/Vtwinpixel p52(tl), Getty Images/Westend61 pp10, 19, 27, 62, Getty Images/Tadao Yamamoto p18(tr), Getty Images/Zero Creatives p44, Getty Images/Zoonar RF p11; **Anna McNuff**/Peter Race p39(bl); **Shutterstock**/Vasyl Shulga p66(tl)

Additional sources: Ryan, R. M. & Deci, E. L. (2000), *Self-determination theory and the facilitation of intrinsic motivation, social development, and well-being*, American Psychologist, (pp55, 68–78), https://dx.doi.org/10.1037/0003-066X.55.1.68, p36; Deci, E. L., & Ryan, R. M. (2012), *Motivation, personality, and development within embedded social contexts: An overview of self-determination theory*, in R. M. Ryan (Ed.), The Oxford Handbook of Human Motivation (pp85–107), Oxford, UK: Oxford University Press, p36; Ryan, R. M. & Deci, E. L. (2017), Self-Determination Theory: Basic Psychological Needs in Motivation, Development, and Wellness, New York: Guilford Publishing, p36

Printed and bound in Argentina

2020
5

Contents

VOCABULARY

Clothes and fashion; Metaphors

A Choose the correct options to complete the sentences.

1 For most of us, it's in our nature to *follow / fit* a trend because being different is so much harder.
2 There's no need to wear a suit when meeting the team leader – *casual / scruffy* clothes will be fine.
3 I wonder where I can find a dressy *uniform / outfit* for Jen's wedding.
4 All it takes is for one influential person to wear something bold and he or she can *set / stand* a new trend.
5 Recently, people have become much more conscious of the type of *costumes / sportswear* they work out in at the gym.
6 One advantage of a school *uniform / costume* is that students who don't have fashionable or designer clothes don't feel left out.
7 Jed wants to be different – he always chooses his clothes so that he *stands / sets* out from the crowd.
8 I can't play tennis after work – I forgot to put my sports *code / gear* in the car.
9 George is a big guy, and he prefers to buy *scruffy / oversized* clothes from a special outlet.
10 I think I need a size smaller – this shirt looks kind of *baggy / scruffy* on me.

B Match the phrases in bold (1–10) in the article with the metaphors, which have the same meaning, in the box below.

are on a tight budget catches your eye for peanuts in the long run make a seamless transition off-the-rack snapped up tailor-made throwing money down the drain wind you up

1 ______
2 ______
3 ______
4 ______
5 ______
6 ______
7 ______
8 ______
9 ______
10 ______

The cool **style guru**

Have you ever wanted to upgrade your look, but felt confused by the range of options available? Does the need to buy dress clothes for work [1]**make you stressed?**

Do you go clothes shopping only to find the best things have already been [2]**bought?** Can't find anything that [3]**appeals to you?** Are you tired of [4]**wasting money** on clothes that just aren't right for you? With us, you can [5]**change effortlessly** from looking, well, let's say not your best – to looking like a million dollars!

We'll match top-quality clothes that'll look good on you immediately but, [6]**eventually,** you'll see just what a difference being well-dressed will make to your prospects.

We have a range of services – from [7]**made in a factory** to [8]**made just for you** – so, even if you [9]**can't spend a lot of money,** we promise to make you look good. We're confident that when you see the results, your life will be transformed, and you will have a wardrobe to be proud of – [10]**for very little money.**

Check out our website for more information!

GRAMMAR
Nominal clauses

A Match numbers (1–6) to letters (a–f) to form full sentences.

1 It should not need pointing out ____
2 The fact that he dresses nicely ____
3 How can something as simple as having an ironed shirt ____
4 For many people, dressing nicely means ____
5 As far as I'm concerned, to look good ____
6 The clothes you wear should not ____

a make a positive impression on others?
b reflects the seriousness with which he treats his position.
c that you have a duty to protect the company's reputation.
d influence others' opinion of you, but they do.
e is to feel good.
f little more than making sure their clothes are new or clean.

B Write one word in each blank to complete the sentences.

1 I think you'll like this jacket, and ______________ may surprise you to learn that it costs less than $40.
2 We are left with the problem of ______________ to address the complaints about our products.
3 The fact ______________ you are employed on a full-time contract gives you certain privileges.
4 I regret ______________ finding out more about the company before I went for an interview there.
5 The reason I objected to the sales clerk ______________ that he had a bad attitude.
6 We may never know the reason ______________ she did what she did.
7 They will be going on vacation in July, but ______________ they're going is still undecided.
8 ______________ you do in your own time is your own affair.

C Complete the second sentence so that it has a similar meaning to the first sentence using the words in bold. Write between two and five words, including the word given.

1 Dissatisfaction with clothing and appearance can be a problem for many these days.
OF
Many people face ______________ dissatisfaction with clothing and appearance.

2 That uniforms are still widely worn in schools is common knowledge.
FACT
______________ uniforms are still widely worn in schools is common knowledge.

3 It's not important what she spends her money on.
HOW
______________ is not important.

4 To wear second-hand clothes is not a problem for me.
MIND
I ______________ second-hand clothes.

PRONUNCIATION
Linking /r/

A Read the sentences aloud, paying attention to the way you pronounce the underlined sections.

1 My <u>car is</u> a lot less expensive than I thought it would be.
2 I <u>wore a</u> suit and felt very stylish.
3 <u>We're already</u> walking to the store.
4 Get one today! <u>They're only</u> $5!
5 I didn't plan to buy anything, but I saw a great shirt <u>for a</u> friend.
6 The things in that boutique <u>are expensive</u>.
7 And <u>you're almost</u> certain you saw that man stealing?
8 I found a <u>hair in</u> my food!

1.1 **B Listen to the sentences from Exercise A. Practice saying the sentences in the same way as the speakers do in the recording.**

GRAMMAR
Comparatives and superlatives

A Choose the correct options to complete the comments about a blog post.

iamthemusicman
2 days ago

I agree with what you say about popular music and originality. But we need to remember that musicians and producers need to attract the listener's attention [1]***as quickly as / quicker than*** possible. Sometimes, this involves producing unusual, trendsetting music, but since listeners don't always react well to [2]***dramatically / marginally*** different styles – at least not at first – it is sometimes safer to work within the boundaries of the [3]***later / latest*** trends.

Like | Comment | Share

fitbit46
5 days ago

I like what you said about music and working out. I'm a fitness instructor and for such activities, I tend to think volume is a factor – my rule is the [4]***louder than / louder*** the volume, the faster the workout. I also think we need music with [5]***a higher / the highest*** rate of beats per minute (bpm) than our heartbeat to help energize us for physical work. However, I don't think increased bpm or volume helps with creative work. [6]***Easily the most / By far the*** creative work is done, in my opinion, when the music is neither too loud nor too quiet, nor too fast nor too slow.

Like | Comment | Share

jazz4life
2 weeks ago

I think our musical tastes can be a good indicator of our personalities. When I was younger, I listened to [7]***the far highest / a considerably higher*** number of hard rock, indie and metal bands. I associate that with a time when I was more introverted but maybe also a lot more creative. Now, I listen to a [8]***great / far*** deal more jazz and soul. I'm a little less creative than I was, but I am a lot more outgoing, sociable and confident. That said, this is probably very subjective. I don't want to make any generalizations as [9]***more deeply / deeper*** analysis is needed to prove any link.

Like | Comment | Share

B Match the beginnings of the sentences (1–8) to the endings (a–h).

1 You're just the best ____
2 I think we have a great deal ____
3 Break for lunch, did you say? That is far ____
4 For some people, having trendy clothes is every bit ____
5 Even if I worked twice ____
6 We agreed that pronunciation is easily ____
7 A greater than ____
8 The upgrade to business class more than ____

a as many hours, I don't think I would get the job done in time.
b and away the best idea I've heard all day.
c and I don't know what I'd do without you.
d more to learn about how our choices are manipulated by marketing people.
e the most difficult aspect of learning English.
f as important as practicality – if not more so.
g made up for the delay to my flight.
h expected number of people attended the event.

VOCABULARY
Experimenting with prefixes and suffixes

A Choose the correct options to complete the sentences.

1 Their online vlog became ***popularish*** / ***hyper-influential*** when they got millions of subscribers.
2 Harry's not very ***tech-savvy*** / ***tech-friendly***. In fact, he can barely use a word processor.
3 Is your watch ***water-prone*** / ***waterproof***? If not, I'd take it off before you go in.
4 That video I made was very ***amateury*** / ***amateurish***, but it was my first one and I've learned a lot of tricks of the trade since then.
5 Ann is so ***disaster-prone*** / ***hyper-disaster***! She broke her phone, TV and tablet all in the same week!
6 Be careful because, once you delete something, you can't ***redelete*** / ***undelete*** it and get it back.
7 I like what the program does, but I don't find it very ***user-friendly*** / ***user-savvy*** – it took me a long time just to learn the basics.
8 Look – you were ***ultra-influential*** / ***super-lucky*** to get this job, so try to make the best of it.

B Rewrite the words in bold by adding a prefix or a suffix. Make any other necessary changes. More than one answer is sometimes possible.

1 These **heat** gloves are perfect for handling hot pans in the kitchen.

____

2 I'm hoping to raise a **large** amount of money to get this business up and running.

____

3 Sara's sick of reading **spam** comments about online articles.

____

4 He was going to buy a house, but he was forced to **think** when he lost his job.

____

5 I thought his jokes were really **cheese**.

____

6 The politician got into trouble because she said something without realizing her microphone had been **muted**.

____

7 Don't worry; this tablet is **idiot**. There's no way you can do any harm by pressing the wrong button.

____

8 They would never take a risk on this investment – you know that they're always **cautious** in their business decisions.

____

PRONUNCIATION
Emphatic stress

1.2 **A Listen to these pairs of sentences. Underline one word in each sentence that has emphatic stress.**

1 He's suggesting one solution, but there are others.
He's suggesting one solution, is that the best he can do?
2 They told me to work on this project, so that's what I'm doing.
They said the same to me, and that's what I am doing.
3 He suggested that the biggest problem is overseas sales.
But you don't realize that the biggest problem is overseas sales.
4 I can do it; the question is whether I want to do it.
I can do it, too, but I don't know when.
5 Do you think this will be a problem?
Without question, this will be a problem.

B Practice saying the sentences in the same way as the speakers do in the recording in Exercise A.

C Decide where to add emphatic stress in these sentences.

1 I was determined not to say anything that could get me in trouble.
2 Contrary to what you said, I do enjoy gardening.
3 Bill got the contract and a promotion, so he's happy.

1.3 **D Listen to check your answers to Exercise C.**

READING

A PREDICT You are going to read an article about selfies. Before you read, answer the questions.

1 Do you post selfies? If so, how often and how many?
2 What do you think motivates people who frequently post selfies?

B READ FOR MAIN IDEA Read *The new narcissism?* and match the paragraphs (1–5) to the summaries of each paragraph (a–e).

Paragraph 1 ____
Paragraph 2 ____
Paragraph 3 ____
Paragraph 4 ____
Paragraph 5 ____

a People who take and post a lot of selfies want to be perceived in a particular way.
b It is not yet clear if selfies are creating cultural change, for example, making people more open or less concerned about privacy.
c While selfies may have a longer history, the availability of technology and equipment is what made them a wider phenomenon in recent years.
d Despite criticism, selfies have been exhibited as a form of art and used to promote it, so it may be premature to say they have a negative impact.
e The first noted use of the word was in the early 2000s. Since then, its usage has steadily increased.

C WORK OUT MEANING Read the article again, paying particular attention to the underlined words (1–6). Find words in the article which have a contrasting meaning.

1 abating ____________
2 hostility ____________
3 ubiquitous ____________
4 plausible ____________
5 mundane ____________, ____________
6 reserved ____________, ____________

D WORK OUT MEANING Now match the words (1–6) to their definitions (a–f).

a seen/done/found everywhere ____
b quiet, not easily showing emotions ____
c believable ____
d becoming less ____
e boring or ordinary ____
f showing opposition or dislike ____

E REFLECT Have you changed your opinion of selfies after reading the article? Why/Why not?

The new NARCISSISM?

Of all the trends created by the digital revolution, one that often divides people is the fad of taking 'selfies'. Some find it baffling, others say it is harmless fun. But we can all agree that after two decades, it seems to be increasing every year rather than [1]abating. So, what do we know about this phenomenon?

1 Where did it come from?

The word 'selfie', it is alleged, originated in Australia. While for the die-hard selfie-haters out there the act of snapping and posting photos might increase feelings of [2]hostility, the use of '-*ie*' or '-*y*' is actually a friendly diminutive. Words like 'barbie' for barbeque or 'Mikey' for 'Michael' are endearing terms and a common feature of spoken English in Australia. The first recorded use of the word is said to be from a young Australian man in a public forum in 2002. In 2013, 'selfie' became the Oxford English Dictionary's word of the year. It is now used in everyday language.

2 Origins and development

Photographs that appear to be taken on devices similar to selfie sticks date back as far as 1926. But selfies really took off with the arrival of the front-facing camera in 2003. Before that, of course, people had been taking pictures of themselves with their cell phones: but selfies as we know them were comparatively rare, whereas now they are [3]ubiquitous. Type in 'selfie' on Instagram and you get close to 300 million results!

3 Look at me!

Is vanity or narcissism really driving this phenomenon? Some would say selfies are not about self-promotion, but simply a way of sharing new experiences with friends and family. The fact that many people post pictures of themselves doing exciting or unusual things makes this explanation seem [4]plausible. But when you consider that people also take pictures of themselves doing [5]mundane things like having breakfast, it seems unlikely it is the whole story. One theory is that it is a way for people to reimagine themselves, to present a different image to the world and to experiment with different identities. It's a way of saying, 'This is how I want to be seen'.

4 Cultural change

The selfie explosion does seem to have had a cultural and social influence. The British, for example, are allegedly perceived of as being [6]reserved, if not actually shy – they are definitely less often described as open or outgoing. Yet the selfie trend has taken hold in the UK as much as anywhere. No doubt, the digital age has encouraged people, especially the young, to make more personal information generally available. I wonder if the era of selfies presents a genuine cultural and social shift, or will there be a reaction against it?

5 Can selfies be art?

This might seem like a silly question. But I have heard one commentator say it is a new 'folk art' that is adding significantly to the language of photography. Exhibits at established galleries have displayed selfies. Whether you agree with this or not, Museum Selfie Day, a trend started by project coordinator Mar Dixon, definitely brings selfie-takers closer to art. In museums and galleries, the public are encouraged to take selfies of themselves in front of famous pieces. In the future, selfies might prove useful to cultural historians interested in the goings-on of people in the early 21st century. Perhaps it's too soon to label this trend as simply a good or a bad thing.

Glossary

alleged (adj) claimed to be true

baffling (adj) confusing, difficult to understand

vanity (n) being too interested in your own appearance

LISTENING

A Imagine that you and your friends are going to make a short video of the previous year's trends, most popular videos, vlogs, etc. What would you include? Give reasons for your answers.

B 1.4 **LISTEN FOR RECOMMENDATIONS** Listen to a conversation between two friends about making a video review of the year. Check (✓) the items which the speakers are going to include.

1 celebrity endorsements ☐
2 viral videos ☐
3 important news stories ☐
4 an image of a TV presenter ☐
5 newspaper headlines ☐
6 cartoons ☐
7 memes ☐
8 home videos of friends ☐
9 clips of influencers/trendsetters ☐

C 1.4 **LISTEN FOR DETAIL** Listen again and complete the sentences with one or two words in each blank.

1 The GenZ video is a ________ of the past year's events.
2 Viewers did not give this year's video positive ________.
3 In one recent viral video, a ________ has an accident.
4 ________ and coloring can be used with pictures of famous people.
5 The woman suggests including short pieces of ________ from movies or cartoons.
6 They decide to include memes which were popular with their ________.
7 As a ________, Daisy Trekker is an influencer, personality and trendsetter.
8 They think it's important to include vlogs that are ________ to draw traffic to their own video.

Glossary

pace (n) speed

viral (adj) very popular and spreading very quickly, especially on the internet

D **REFLECT** Are internet trendsetters more influential than traditional role models such as movies, music, TV stars or athletes? Why/Why not?

1.5 Trends

Write a blog post

WRITING

A You are going to read a blog post. Before you read, think about these questions.

1. How does a blog post differ from other kinds of writing?
2. What features do you think would make a blog post more attractive to readers?
3. What can you do to improve the ranking of a blog or website?

B Read *4 tips for a successful blog post* and match the headings (a–d) to the paragraphs (1–4).

a. Structure your posts
b. Grow your blog
c. Think before you write
d. Know your audience, know yourself

C **MAKING YOUR BLOG POST SUCCESSFUL** Read the blog post again and answer the questions.

1. What are the keywords (the most frequently repeated words) in the tips?
2. How will organizing your blog post in the way advised improve search engine-friendliness?
3. What else can be done to attract more readers?
4. What 'call to action' does the writer use at the end of the post?

WRITING PRACTICE

A **PREPARE** You are going to write a blog post about a current trend. Choose from this list, or use your own idea. Write notes about your chosen topic.

- fashion (clothes)
- a personal item
- a new gadget
- recreational activity
- superhero movies

B **PLAN** Organize your notes from Exercise A into a plan.

- Use an appropriate structure for a blog post (including paragraph headings).
- Think about who your target audience is.
- Choose a keyword or phrase for repetition.

C **WRITE** Write your article in 200–300 words. Use your plan to help you.

4 TIPS FOR A SUCCESSFUL BLOG POST

A successful blog post needs to be both search engine-friendly and reader-friendly. The two go together, and by following these tips, you will enhance your online profile and produce more successful blog posts.

1 __

What exactly is the purpose of your blog? What is your message? And what action do you want people to take when they've finished reading? Think about these points and write some notes.

2 __

Successful blog posts have a clear target audience and their message is tailored accordingly. This means thinking about what will attract your readers' attention but also drawing in the curious browser. This also means working out what *your* selling point is. Is it your expertise, your passion for the subject, your taste, style or personal viewpoint? Build on your strengths.

3 __

Successful blog posts are well-organized. Obvious, I know, but many posts read as if the writer just wrote the first thing that came into their head. Every post should have:

- an introduction
- a main body
- a conclusion.

Write notes about what you want to put in each section. This is a summary of your post – now you can start to fill it in. It is a feature of successful blog posts that they give each paragraph an informative and eye-catching heading using keywords. This is important because the search engine will pick up the main topics and help to improve your ranking.

4 __

To increase both your readership and your position on the search engine, add links to previous posts on the same topic, and keep adding posts to your website so your audience and the search engine know you're still there.

For more tips on writing a successful blog post, click on the icon below.

Click here

VOCABULARY
Describing art

A Match the adjectives (1–8) to the definitions (a–h).

1 tedious ___
2 appalling ___
3 hilarious ___
4 thought-provoking ___
5 groundbreaking ___
6 unconventional ___
7 overrated ___
8 pretentious ___

a different from what people think is usual
b dreadful, awful
c extremely funny
d new and pioneering, innovative
e not as good as people say
f attempts to impress with qualities it doesn't have
g very boring
h makes you think

B Choose the correct words to complete the sentences.

1 An artist doesn't necessarily have to be ***groundbreaking / appalling*** to make good art.
2 Many hyped blockbusters are actually ***imaginative / overrated*** and disappointing.
3 Personally I found the movie ***pretentious / sensational*** – it felt like the director was just trying to show off how clever she is.
4 We think the play was supposed to be serious, but the acting was so bad it was actually ***iconic / hilarious***.
5 The painter's style is very ***tedious / unconventional*** – there is nobody that paints in the same way.
6 The painting is truly ***pretentious / thought-provoking*** – it makes you think about how we live in the modern world.
7 What a ***sensational / overrated*** performance by the lead actor – one of the best I've ever seen.
8 It was so ***groundbreaking / tedious*** – 90 minutes and nothing happens at all!

C Complete the text with the adjectives in the box.

acclaimed appalling iconic repetitive sensational underrated

Caroline Duncan's [1] ________ exhibit is making quite a few headlines and attracting fans worldwide. And they are right to describe it as fantastic. In her groundbreaking work, Duncan combines different art forms, including painting, film, photography and writing, to tell the story of a fictional family's journey from Lebanon to Paris.

The first section includes [2] ________ images and film footage of the Eiffel Tower in Paris from the 1970s. Real footage is mixed with fiction to create a film that shows the mundane and [3] ________ work and chores the family need to do as they struggle with [4] ________ poverty. We then explore the inner world of the characters through diaries, poetry and stories. In my view, Caroline Duncan is vastly [5] ________ as an artist, but I feel that that is about to change. She deserves to be much more highly [6] ________ for her work.

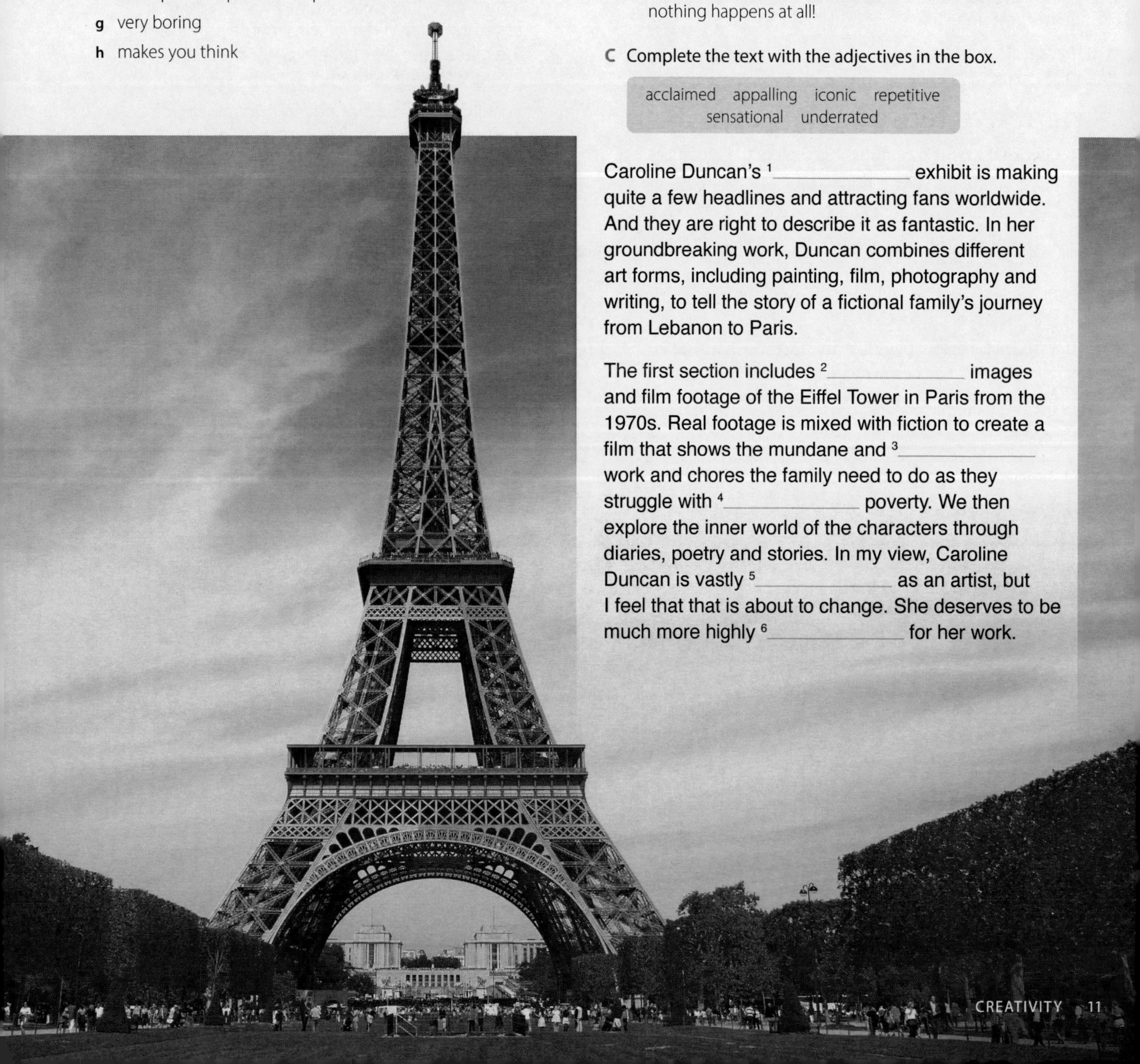

PRONUNCIATION
Contrastive stress

A Read the sentences aloud, paying attention to the contrastive stress on the underlined words.

1. Actually, I like a lot of modern art – it's abstract art I have difficulty with.
2. Why don't we go to the theater for a change, since we always go to the movies?
3. Although everyone says the new play is great, I found it very tedious.
4. I don't like opera, but I'm very interested in ballet.
5. While your eyes are drawn to the middle, what happens at the front is more exciting.
6. The movie was more of a romance than a thriller.
7. I much prefer landscape paintings – I'm not a fan of portraits.
8. No, I prefer listening to recorded music, not live music.

2.1 **B** Listen to the sentences from Exercise A. Practice saying the sentences in the same way as the speakers do in the recording.

GRAMMAR
Narrative tenses

A Choose the correct options to complete the sentences.

1. The exhibit space *was being prepared* / *was preparing* for the big opening when we arrived.
2. I jumped up the moment they *were calling* / *called* my name.
3. Everyone *was waiting* / *had waited* in suspense for the result to be announced.
4. We didn't stay at our usual hotel because it *was being damaged* / *had been damaged* in a fire the week before.
5. I was tired when I got home because I *have had* / *had had* to stay very late at work.
6. We *were telling* / *were told* the results would come out the following week.
7. Why *wasn't I informed* / *didn't I inform* about the change of plan?
8. The road was dangerous because it *had been snowing* / *has been snowing* during the night.

B Find and correct eight mistakes in the text. Sometimes more than one correct answer is possible.

Thursday May 23, 2019

THE MEETING

So – big day today. Important meeting with some clients so I had to get to the office early. I got up at five, had a quick cup of coffee and had left the house at 5:20. I got half way to the office when I realized that I had been forgetting my phone. Can you believe it? I drove for at least half an hour already, so I really didn't feel like going back, but I was having no choice. So, that delayed me by about an hour.

And when I finally got to the office, I gave a message that my boss wanted to see me urgently. I ran to her office. I could see through the glass door she talked to my clients, who already arrived. Oh no!

Luckily, she wasn't annoyed and my clients were fine. The meeting went well, and by lunchtime, we have agreed on everything.

VOCABULARY
Ideas and inspiration; Compound adjectives

A Complete the magazine interview with one word in each blank. The first letter is given to help you.

Do you find it hard to get started on a new project?

It takes time, yes. Of course, having the idea to begin with is the important part. If I know what I want to paint or sculpt, I'm eager to get started. But sometimes, I hit a [1]**w**__________ – I just have no ideas at all. When I'm – quite literally – working from a blank [2]**c**__________ right at the start of a project, I get a bit stressed.

What do you do when you're not inspired? How do you jump [3]s__________ your creativity?

I usually [4]**d**__________ inspiration from other artists. I go to galleries, look at pictures online, that sort of thing. I get a [5]**f**__________ perspective on things in that way. Sometimes I [6]**b**__________ ideas off friends and then I [7]**r**__________ with an idea. For me, it's important to communicate with other people, but then, to get into the right [8]**s**__________ of mind, I need to be alone. I [9]**t**__________ my instincts and it's never long before I'm working again.

Can you describe what happens when you get started?

That's when you won't see me for days – possibly weeks! I totally [10]**i**__________ myself in my work. During that time, nothing else matters. I would forget to eat if people didn't bring me food!

B Choose the correct options to complete the sentences.

1 Jim works long hours in the studio so he often listens to ***part / late***-night radio programs.

2 Ken got a ***part / self***-time job while studying for his doctorate.

3 In the acting world, you need to be ***thick / self***-skinned because you can get more criticism than praise sometimes.

4 I wouldn't like to be ***part / self***-employed. I'm happy working for my boss.

5 Flora left school and found a ***world / highly*** paid job with a TV production company.

6 Let's face it – the chances of anyone becoming a ***well / world***-famous singer are pretty slim.

7 I try to remain ***open / late***-minded about my job. If they offered me a transfer to a different branch, I like to think I would consider it.

8 If you work for yourself, you need to be a ***well / open***-motivated worker because it's tempting to take it easy.

PRONUNCIATION
Questions for comment or criticism

A Read the conversation aloud, paying attention to the intonation at the end of the questions.

Woman: Jake from our creative writing course says that he gets all his ideas in his dreams!

Man: Is he crazy? Dreams are so random. And I wouldn't be able to remember mine anyway.

Woman: He keeps a dream diary by his bed. That's a good idea, don't you think?

Man: How can you keep a diary of dreams? Dreams don't make any sense.

Woman: Aren't you being a bit negative? The diary might work for him and help with his stories.

Man: Who writes about dreaming? You need to write about something you actually know or have experienced. Isn't that the point?

Woman: Are you serious? Writing isn't just about what we know. Anyway I've started a diary myself. I set an alarm for the middle of the night. So, I can wake up in the middle of the dream.

Man: Why would you do that? You'll just be tired and feel even less creative the next day. Better to sleep well and then actually come up with some interesting ideas yourself.

Woman: Isn't that a bit dismissive? And why don't you read some of his stories before you decide it's a bad idea?

B (2.2) Listen to the conversation from Exercise A. Then practice reading it in the same way as the speakers do in the recording.

GRAMMAR
Future in the past

A **Match the beginnings of the sentences (1–6) to the endings (a–f).**

1 We were going ___
2 Meeting Stella would ___
3 They were to ___
4 I was just ___
5 We weren't ___
6 Jenny and Fiona ___

a supposed to use the computer for personal use, but nobody said anything.
b about to go out when I got a phone call.
c were going on vacation the next day so they were packing.
d to call you, but we thought you might be sleeping.
e turn out to be an unforgettable experience.
f call us if there was any kind of problem.

B **Choose the correct options (a, b or c) to complete the sentences.**

1 The bridge ___ been completed last year but there were unexpected delays.
a was to have
b was
c had to have

2 You ___ finish the reports before four o'clock. What happened?
a were about to
b would
c were supposed to

3 Sorry – I interrupted you. You ___ something?
a were about to say
b would have said
c weren't supposed to say

4 We were ___ go on vacation when we heard the news.
a about just to
b just about to
c about to just

5 Who thought it ___ a good idea to play a trick on me?
a would be
b will be
c had been

6 We knew he ___ a famous singer.
a was always being
b was always going to be
c had always supposed to be

7 You had your instructions – you ___ me the minute you arrived.
a were calling
b were about to call
c were to call

8 I didn't have much time with John because he ___ for Brazil the next day.
a had been leaving
b was leaving
c would have left

READING

A PREDICT Look at the title of the article and the picture. Which words from the word cloud below do you think will appear in the article?

map **pilot** **engineer** bridge
creativity proposal **perspective** railway
carriage flag **survey** **overground**
construction **canvas**

B READ FOR GIST Read *The channel tunnel* quickly. Why did it take so long to create this transportation link between Britain and France?

C READ FOR DETAIL Read again and answer the questions.

1. Who put forward the first plan for a transportation link between the two countries?
2. Which proposal after 1979 did not involve an underwater tunnel?
3. How long did it take to build the tunnel?

D INFER MEANING Read the article again and choose the correct answer (a or b).

1. What do you understand by the use of the phrase 'finally agreed'? (Paragraph 1)
   - **a** The writer is unhappy about the tunnel.
   - **b** It had taken a long time to reach an agreement.
2. Why did engineers 'study the blueprints' despite problems between the two countries? (Paragraph 2)
   - **a** They had made a secret agreement with the authorities.
   - **b** They still believed that the project would be completed one day.
3. What can we infer from the sentence 'One British and one French worker were chosen by lottery to be the first to greet each other …'?
   - **a** France and Britain wanted to be seen as equals in the project.
   - **b** The workers wanted to congratulate each other.

E REFLECT Think about the answers to these questions.

1. Do you believe that this project was worth the time and money spent on it? Why/Why not?
2. What other impressive engineering projects, ancient or modern, can you name?

THE CHANNEL TUNNEL

It was in 1985 that British and French governments finally agreed to construct a tunnel under the English Channel. It would be one of the largest engineering projects undertaken by the UK. But the talks had begun a long time before that – since at least 1957 when Louis Armand's study group came up with a proposal for two railway tunnels, with a third smaller tunnel for maintenance running between them.

But dreams of a link between England and France go back even further than that. The first proposal was made by a French mining engineer, Albert Mathieu, at the beginning of the 19th century, who suggested a road tunnel that allowed horse-drawn carriages to pass between the two countries. When hostilities broke out between the English and the French, the plan was abandoned. Engineers continued to study the blueprints, however, and thought they could adapt their recently acquired expertise in building overground tunnels to building one under water.

By 1871, England and France were on friendly terms again and further surveys were completed, and this time, they got as far as deciding where to start tunneling. However, this plan, too, had to be abandoned following a change of government in England.

On several occasions over the next 100 years, the project looked as if it might be revived. But it wasn't until the 1970s that another serious attempt was made, when both sides agreed to start digging. However, this was stopped for economic reasons. A change in government in 1979 brought the project back to life. Although this time, there would be no public funding, so it had to be privately financed. The Channel Tunnel Company won the contract, with the same 1960 three-tunnels-in-one idea. Other proposals included: Eurobridge (a suspension bridge) and Euroute (a sea tunnel joining man-made islands).

Construction began in 1988 at Folkestone in England and Coquelles in France simultaneously, the idea being to meet in the middle. It turned into a race to see who could get there first. Tunnel-drilling machines, weighing 1000 tons and needing about 20 people to operate, were used to drill through the rock and chalk layers. After two years, the tunnels met in the middle. One British and one French worker were chosen by lottery to be the first to greet each other when the breakthrough was made.

This tremendous engineering project was finally completed by May 1994. It is now considered to be one of the seven wonders of the modern world.

Glossary

blueprint (n) a drawing or plan showing how to build a machine/building, etc
drill (v) to make a hole using a special machine/tool
ventilation (n) a system allowing fresh air to move around a building

LISTENING

A PREDICT Put the words in the correct columns. Which of these words would you use to describe the building in the picture?

appalling awesome groundbreaking iconic pretentious sensational thought-provoking unconventional

Positive	Negative	Neither positive nor negative

B ANTICIPATE CONTENT You are going to listen to part of a radio program called *Frank Gehry: life and work*. Look again at the picture in Exercise A. Answer the questions.

1 What is Frank Gehry's profession?
2 How successful is he?
3 Is his style traditional or unconventional?
4 Think of another question you expect to be answered in the program.

2.3 **C LISTEN FOR GIST** Listen to the program and check your predictions in Exercise B.

2.3 **D LISTEN FOR DETAIL** Listen again and complete the sentences with one or two words in each blank. Sometimes more than one answer is possible.

1 These days, architects like famous artists get admiration and ______.
2 While Gehry takes satisfaction in his achievements, he is not fond of ______.
3 Before achieving fame, Gehry had to deal with ______.
4 Gehry felt strongly that his buildings should mirror their ______.
5 Gehry is able to create striking and distinctive shapes through building with ______.
6 People who visit the Guggenheim Museum have been known to say that the building is ______ than the things in it.

Glossary

be a household name (phr) be very well-known
commission (n) a request for an artist to create a piece of work (for payment)
discipline (n) a subject that people study
signature style (n) style which is associated with a particular person

E REFLECT Think about the answers to these questions.

1 What style of architecture do you like (for example, modern or traditional)? Why?
2 Think about a famous building in your country. How would you describe it? Use the adjectives in Exercise A.

WRITING

A Which of these places would you most enjoy visiting and why?

- a gallery with works by unknown, living artists
- an exhibit of a well-known painter
- a museum with interesting objects from the past

B Read *Monet at the National Gallery* and match the paragraphs (1–5) to the brief paragraph summaries (a–e).

a the writer's opinion of the exhibit ___
b introducing the exhibit and its theme ___
c a more detailed look at the paintings ___
d how the exhibit is arranged ___
e revisiting the theme of the exhibit ___

Monet
at the National Gallery

1 When you mention the name 'Monet', most people think 'water lilies', but this exhibit is entitled 'Monet and Architecture', which is not a connection most art lovers would make. French Impressionist painter Monet painted Rouen Cathedral several times and there are buildings in many of his paintings, but … architecture as an important theme?

2 Organized in such a way as to surprise and delight the visitor, the paintings are presented in an unusual fashion. You don't go from room to room looking at his early, middle and late periods; the idea is more than that you see how his later work was influenced by his early work. Monet, born in 1840, continued painting until the mid-1920s, so there is much to explore.

3 Examples of the Rouen Cathedral paintings are here, somehow making the weighty and massive construction seem ready to float away. This is also true of the Venice paintings. Already part of a floating city, the buildings of Venice seem to sail like gondolas on the water. There are paintings done in London, too, a city about which Monet boldly said, 'would be quite ugly if not for the fog'.

4 Buildings, though, are often just a focus point for other elements of the work, a point from which the eye is drawn into the painting. They are just another part of nature, subject to the same laws and conditions. You will come away with a sense of extraordinary beauty and the passing of time.

5 This is a wonderful exhibit that I would recommend to everyone – art lover or not. If you only know Monet for his water lilies, you don't know half the story.

C **WRITING CONCISELY** Find sentences or clauses in the review which express these ideas in a more concise way. Match each one to a grammatical feature.

1 The paintings are organized in such a way as to surprise and delight the visitor and are presented in an unusual fashion. ___
2 Monet, who was born in 1840, continued painting until the mid-1920s … ___
3 Monet was a French Impressionist painter who painted Rouen Cathedral several times … ___

a noun phrase
b reduced adjective clause
c participle clause

WRITING PRACTICE

A **PREPARE** You are going to write a review of a cultural or artistic event. Think about the answers to these questions and write notes.

1 Have you been to a cultural or artistic event recently (art/photography exhibit, museum, concert, book reading, etc)?
2 Where was it? What was on display or what happened? If it was an exhibit, who was the main artist? Was there a theme?
3 How was the event organized? How were the artworks / museum objects / different aspects presented?
4 What did you like or dislike about the event?

B **PLAN** Organize your notes from Exercise A into a plan.

- Use an appropriate structure for a review.
- Don't forget to give your recommendation in the last paragraph.

C **WRITE** Write your review in 220–260 words. Use your plan to help you.

3.1 Progress

Progressive design

VOCABULARY
Sustainability; Forming verbs from adjectives

A Choose the correct options to complete the article.

AIR POLLUTION

When it comes to air pollution, by far the worst [1]***depletions / emissions*** are those created by power stations which we use for electricity production. Some people seem to think that their activities are [2]***biodegradable / carbon-neutral*** just because they plant a few trees to [3]***consume / offset*** the damage caused by flying all over the world, but airplanes are not the cause of the worst damage.

We tend to think of electricity as clean and harmless because that is the form in which it seems to arrive in our homes – after all, we don't see the smoke pouring out of power stations because they are usually far from where we live. We sometimes conveniently 'forget' that fossil fuels aren't [4]***degradable / sustainable*** forms of energy, so we rarely consider our [5]***over-exploitation / over-emission*** of coal, oil and gas and the [6]***depletion / emission*** of these limited natural resources.

It is easy to ignore the waste we produce which is not [7]***biodegradable / bio-sustainable***, but is in fact poisonous and ends up accumulating in the air, the soil and the water.

The use of [8]***degradable / renewable*** energy, such as from wind, rain, sunlight, waves and geothermal heat, solves many of these problems.

B Complete the sentences with the verb form of the adjectives in parentheses.

1 Recent research shows that if you ________ (*visual*) your preferred outcome in any given situation, it can improve your chances of success.

2 Top analysts have warned that the current economic crisis will ________ (*deep*) if the government doesn't introduce a new investment program.

3 It's a good idea to ________ (*empty*) your 'recycle bin' frequently as too many deleted files can slow down your computer.

4 Designers in China have developed robots which can absorb carbon dioxide and ________ (*pure*) polluted city air.

5 Conducting a cost-benefit analysis will ________ (*able*) us to decide whether the company should expand its activities into the construction sector.

6 I believe that if we ________ (*simple*) the application process, then more people will be encouraged to take part in the volunteer program.

7 Most people agree that spending time working or studying in another country ________ (*broad*) our understanding of other cultures.

8 Government officials hope that the international business conference will help to ________ (*strong*) ties with their European colleagues.

GRAMMAR
Future structures

A Match each rule to an example sentence.

1. We use future progressive to describe a situation that will be in progress at a particular point in the future or to emphasize that it will cover an extended period of time. ___
2. We use future perfect to describe changes that will be completed before a particular point in the future. ___
3. We use future perfect progressive to focus on the future results of an earlier future process and/or measure the length of time of that process. ___
4. After words like *if*, *when*, *while*, etc, future tenses usually become present tenses. ___
5. Other future structures include *be on the brink of (doing)* and *be about / due / set to (do)*. ___

a. Unless my new passport comes tomorrow, I won't be able to go on vacation!
b. This time next week, we'll be taking our exam.
c. Some astrophysicists believe they're on the verge of a very exciting discovery.
d. By the time they get to Mars, they'll have been traveling for over nine months.
e. They'll have finished painting the walls by tomorrow.

B Match the beginnings of the sentences (1–8) to the endings (a–h).

1. By the time I graduate, I will ___
2. The agreement is set to ___
3. By my 18th birthday, I will ___
4. I expect we'll be ___
5. The company is on the ___
6. I might have ___
7. The meeting is due ___
8. I'll be studying for my geography exam while ___

a. be signed before the end of the year.
b. brink of being sold to its biggest competitor.
c. you're relaxing on the beach!
d. have been studying for nearly five years!
e. to take place in Paris on Tuesday.
f. have visited at least 30 countries.
g. seeing more of each other now we're living so close.
h. finished my work by eight o'clock. I'll call you if I have.

PRONUNCIATION
Sounding persuasive

A Decide if each sentence is an example of exceptionalism (A), empathy (B) or flattery (C).

1. I can tell you're a good judge of character! ___
2. Maybe I can get you a special deal – just let me speak to my boss for a moment. ___
3. Well, we all have to watch what we spend these days, don't we? ___
4. You look like someone who takes very good care of himself. Do you work out? ___
5. I know *exactly* what you mean! ___
6. Wow, that's a very good question. Nobody's ever asked me that before. ___

B Read the sentences from Exercise A aloud. Try to sound as persuasive as possible. Remember that you can do this by speaking more loudly/quietly or faster/slower and using rising or falling intonation.

3.1 **C Listen to the sentences from Exercise A. Practice saying the sentences in the same way as the speakers do in the recording.**

PRONUNCIATION
Stress-shift words

A Look at the words in bold and decide if they are verbs or nouns.

1 If you **rewrite** the essay without the **extracts**, I **suspect** your score will **increase** because it has a lot of positive **attributes**.

2 Ignoring his **protests**, the judge **rejected** his appeal because his **conduct** had been so poor, but he was **transferred** to an open prison and he was **permitted** to have access to a computer.

3 We asked the singer what he **attributed** his success to, and he said that he had **progressed** in the business because he hadn't given up, even when he had been publicly **insulted** in the press.

4 I didn't like these computers at first, but now I'm a **convert** and I plan to do some **research** to find out if I can **upgrade** my own at a reasonable price.

5 The island doesn't have many **exports** and they **import** a lot of goods, so the prices are much higher after **transportation** costs have been added.

6 Reports **conflict** as to whether the **conflict** was started by ticket holders or the security guards.

B Underline the part of each bold word in Exercise A which is stressed.

3.2 **C** Listen to the sentences to check your answers in Exercise B.

GRAMMAR
Negative inversion

A Find and correct the mistakes in the sentences.

1 Not only Jake was a good businessman, but he was also a kind person.

____

2 No sooner had we arrived when it started to rain.

____

3 By no means this is over.

____

4 Under no circumstances you must disturb me.

____

5 Not once they said thank you.

____

6 No way I am ever going back there!

____

7 Only after I insisted replaced they the broken phone.

____

8 Not since I was a child I have felt so excited.

____

B Complete the extract from a story with one word in each blank. Sometimes more than one correct answer is possible.

They had told Alex when he was younger that the surveillance was for everybody's good. It was a mark of progress, to keep everybody safe – nothing to be feared. But today was the first time he had actually been followed – at least, he thought it was.

[1] ____________ in a million years did he imagine he was important enough to be followed! Yet no [2] ____________ had he stepped off the number 7 bus than he realized that the guy was there again, the same middle-aged man wearing glasses and a leather jacket. Not [3] ____________ had Alex seen him at lunchtime outside the restaurant, but he had also seen him when he arrived at work in the morning. Now, hardly had Alex reached the end of his street when he was struck by a terrible realization, 'No way [4] ____________ I want him to see where I live!' he thought.

Acting as naturally as possible, Alex crossed over and, turning right, started heading away from his house. Only [5] ____________ he had walked for another five minutes did he risk looking over his shoulder. The man had gone. Alex didn't have enough information to assume the worst, but [6] ____________ was he prepared to go home just yet. Under [7] ____________ circumstances did he want the man to find out his address. But as night started to fall, Alex realized that he didn't have a Plan B.

VOCABULARY
Verb–noun collocations

A Choose the correct options to complete the sentences.

1 In some areas the tourism industry can ***make / do*** more harm than good.

2 The business did badly last year and we've ***seen / delivered*** little progress so far this year.

3 You're just ***demonstrating / perpetuating*** the myth that all volunteers want is a free vacation.

4 If you get offered a place on that course, you should ***make / seize*** the opportunity.

5 If the manager doesn't ***set / attain*** clear objectives, how can the staff know what to do?

6 I don't think we're going to ***succeed / achieve*** our sales goals this month.

7 If you ***made / did*** a concerted effort, you might get the job finished on time.

8 When the factory opens in the village, it will ***take / bring*** benefits to the whole community.

B Complete the sentences with the verbs in the box.

brought displayed made make perpetuate seize set take

1 We've ________ great advances in technology since the turn of the century.

2 TV programs often ________ stereotypes about different social groups.

3 The figures ________ an imbalance and we began to suspect theft.

4 You know, we're always going to ________ limited progress unless we change the management structure.

5 Do you think the new factory has ________ more benefits to the area than problems?

6 I think this is a golden opportunity which we need to ________ with both hands.

7 I think you'll like him if you ________ the time to get to know him.

8 I probably failed because I hadn't ________ realistic goals for myself.

READING

A PREDICT You are going to read an article about the pros and cons of technological progress. Before you read, answer the questions.

1 What areas of life have benefitted most from technological progress?

2 What might be some long-term problems caused by technological progress?

B READ FOR GIST Read *The cost of progress*. Were any of your ideas from Exercise A mentioned?

C READ FOR COSTS AND BENEFITS Read *The cost of progress*. What are the costs and benefits in these areas of technological progress? Write notes to complete the table.

	Benefits	Costs
Communications		
Medicine		
Industry		

D REFLECT Choose one of the areas discussed in the article. Do you think the benefits of technological progress outweigh the costs? Why/Why not?

Glossary

by-product (n) an unintended result
etch (v) to delineate or impress clearly
longevity (n) the fact of living a long life

The cost of progress

From voice-activated speakers to endless options for online socializing, sharing and posting, it's clear that many of us are enjoying the benefits of technology. At the same time, we're hearing more voices that raise concerns at the rate of technological development and our lack of forward thinking about the potential costs it may bring.

To consider the balance between benefits and costs, we looked at three areas of technological and scientific progress: communications, industry and medicine.

Many people can't live without their phones, the new computers in their hands. Smartphone users continue to increase worldwide. Phones enable us to keep in touch with family, friends and colleagues with ease. But are these advantages perhaps superficial? Are they simply what people have always done but on a much larger scale? Well, not really – phone technology now does so much more, allowing us to navigate, shop, entertain ourselves, record our vacations and socialize in an endless stream of new ways. And many businesses couldn't function without this technology as rapid communication broadens their area of operations, as well as speeding their business up.

But has anything been lost along the way? Having grown up in a world before cell phones, I'm acutely aware of the random strings of numbers still etched in my memory. The landline from my friend's parents, for example. I think I can live without this information but are we losing our capacity to memorize or do simple calculations? Even if this may not seem very dramatic, what if it is a symptom of a general loss of mental skills? Could it affect the whole learning process?

In medicine, technology has improved healthcare enormously. In some countries, it's now possible to see a doctor online if required. Operations can be performed by robots, guided by doctors at a distance. Research into diseases – aided by technology – has brought new medicines to combat and even prevent them, though at some expense. There's no doubting both the short- and long-term benefits for individuals in this case. And yet, increasing longevity does raise new concerns and issues. We need to address how to finance pensions and ensure adequate care for older people. We also need to consider any negative impact that healthier older people may have on the job market. If people work longer, will it limit opportunities for younger workers?

Technology has improved efficiency in industry. A by-product of machines doing the heavy and repetitive work is that people don't have to do this. However, this means that skills which have been handed down through the generations are slowly being lost. Automation is good for the economy of the country as a whole and sometimes allows governments to spend more on social and engineering projects. The downside is that more and more jobs being done by machines may mean more and more people out of work, unless we as a society are able to quickly adapt to the harsh realities of retraining or working a shorter working week.

The scientific and technological progress we see taking place today is awe-inspiring – both wonderful and frightening. While the benefits of technology are unquestionable and life has improved for millions of people, we can't ignore the potential costs that progress brings. The need for more radical technological regulation could become greater in the future.

LISTENING

A If you were going to undertake voluntary work, which of these projects would you choose and why?

- helping to clean a beach
- working in a youth/community center
- helping to protect wild animals

3.3 B **LISTEN FOR TECHNIQUES** Listen to a conversation about a 'voluntourism' project in Tanzania and check (✓) the sentences you hear.

1 I bet you know a lot about important social and environmental issues, right? ☐
2 It's probably *the* most important event in the calendar. ☐
3 I can see you're a very smart guy. ☐
4 You're a kind-hearted person, aren't you? ☐
5 I'm *so* glad you asked. ☐
6 Just imagine the view from there. ☐
7 Can you visualize that? ☐
8 It's *absolutely* stunning! ☐
9 I really appreciate it. ☐
10 How good is that? ☐

C Which of the sentences that you checked in Exercise B make use of a persuasive technique? Is it exaggeration, a leading question or personalization?

3.3 D **LISTEN FOR SPECIFIC INFORMATION** Listen again. Decide if the statements are true (T) or false (F).

1 Steven feels disappointed because there is too much information. T / F
2 Joanna says she has spoken to many people visiting the Expo already. T / F
3 If Steven travels to Tanzania, he will help to build a school. T / F
4 Steven's lack of building skills is not a problem. T / F
5 The accommodations provided will not be luxurious. T / F
6 Steven would prefer to be paid for his work on the project. T / F
7 Steven will pay for food, accommodations, flights and administration costs. T / F
8 Joanna succeeds in persuading Steven to sign up for the trip. T / F

Glossary

bricklaying (n) building walls using bricks

E **REFLECT** Would it be easy for a salesperson to persuade you to buy something? Why/Why not?

WRITING

A Read the email and answer the questions.

1 Who do you think Gerry Pierce is?

______

2 Who is he writing to?

______

3 What is the purpose of his email?

______

B **PERSUASIVE TECHNIQUES** Read the email again and write the number of a paragraph (1–5) next to each persuasive technique (a–e). You will use one paragraph twice.

a using fact and figures ___
b appeal to readers' fears ___
c flattery ___ ___
d using technical terms ___
e linking weaknesses with strengths ___

WRITING PRACTICE

A **PREPARE** You are going to write a persuasive email about introducing new technology, equipment or ideas into a work environment. Think about the answers to these questions and write notes.

1 What is the work environment: business, educational, hospital, recreational, other?
2 What is your role?
3 Who are you writing to?
4 What are you persuading them to introduce?

B **PLAN** Organize your notes from Exercise A into a plan.

- Use an appropriate structure for a persuasive email.
- Use the techniques for persuasion from Writing Exercise B.

C **WRITE** Write your email in 220–260 words. Use your plan to help you.

To: Teachers' Workroom
From: Gerry Pierce
Subject: Interactive whiteboards

Dear All,

1 As you know, I have been pressing the Board of Directors to upgrade our classrooms for some time now. Thanks to your efforts, this college has an excellent academic record and reputation. Yet I notice some potential students' disappointment when they are shown around the facilities and see that we are behind the times with regard to the latest educational tools.

2 I know that some of you have doubts about the upgrades, mainly regarding costs and how it might affect your jobs. But I would also remind you that no teacher wants to be left behind either. Smart classrooms are becoming the new standard. We risk losing potential students and also making our job prospects worse if we do not keep up.

3 You'd be surprised at how much we spend on dry marker pens, erasers, chalks and blackboard painting each year. Interactive whiteboards need none of these things. Equipped with the latest LCD touchscreen displays with striking visuals and graphics, these boards have everything in one place to enhance learning. If we can get the go-ahead, there will be training sessions for us all. Most students these days are tech-savvy, so you can always ask them for help if you get stuck!

4 Although acquiring interactive whiteboards will require some initial investment, we will benefit in the long run by saving on teaching materials and attracting more students (see attached costs/benefits analysis). The new equipment would bring more ease and flexibility to the learning experience and will make it more interesting and fun for both students and teachers.

5 I am pleased to work with some of the smartest and best trained teachers at Broadwick College. You deserve better. So let's get together on this and equip the college with smart classrooms. With your support, I'm sure the Board will be persuaded to provide the funds to bring us into the 21st century, so I ask each one of you to reply to this email stating your commitment to my proposals.

Best regards,

Gerry

PRONUNCIATION
Adding information

A Read the pairs of sentences (a and b) aloud. Try to step down to a lower pitch when you read the underlined information in sentence b.

1 a A lot of people say that eating superfoods can make you more intelligent.
b A lot of people say that eating superfoods – <u>which include fish, broccoli, nuts and spinach</u> – can make you more intelligent.

2 a Generally speaking, exercise can help you stay more alert.
b Generally speaking, exercise – <u>even something gentle like walking or stretching</u> – can help you stay more alert.

3 a Starting work early in the morning is meant to make you more productive.
b Starting work early in the morning, <u>as opposed to working late into the evening</u>, is meant to make you more productive.

4 a Some people are great believers in 'mindfulness'.
b Some people are great believers in mindfulness, <u>the practice of living in the moment without thinking about the past or worrying about the future</u>.

4.1 **B** Listen to the sentences from Exercise A. Practice saying the sentences in the same way as the speakers do in the recording.

VOCABULARY
Conceptual metaphors

A Match the sentences (1–7) to the related conceptual metaphors (a–e). You will need to use some of the letters more than once.

1 Tim had always been eager to get ahead, but now his career had reached a dead end. ___
2 Unlike her sister, who obviously had a brilliant mind, Stella came across as less bright. ___
3 I've invested countless hours in this business – I won't let it fail. ___
4 My suggestions for the new project were shot down in flames. ___
5 Don't make her angry – she has a really fiery temper. ___
6 Carl lost his cool and threw the folder across the room. ___
7 I could tell as he listened to my speech that he was getting ready to attack. ___

a time = money
b anger = heat
c argument = war
d life = journey
e light = intelligence

B Complete the story with the words in the box.

attack	backwards	cool	crossroads
defenseless	shed	tempered	wasted

Sarah felt she had reached a [1] ________ in her life. Everything depended on her winning this business negotiation. She knew if she wasn't successful it would be a huge step [2] ________ for her. At the very least, she would have [3] ________ the last year.

The key thing would be to get her client Ricardo on her side. He was very hot-[4] ________ at the best of times, and people often felt [5] ________ when he really went on the attack. A conversation with her colleague Patricia [6] ________ a lot of light on how she should approach Ricardo.

Although she was nervous on the day of the negotiation, she successfully kept her [7] ________. She was so calm and diplomatic that Ricardo didn't even realize she was implementing a careful plan of [8] ________.

The negotiation was a success. Of course both sides won. But Sarah won a little more than Ricardo this time.

4.1 Intelligence

Brain training

GRAMMAR
Conditionals without *if*

A Choose the correct options (a, b or c) to complete the sentences.

1 ____ you had $1 million – what would you do first?
   a Were
   b Imagine
   c Should

2 Ask a random sample of people if they are intelligent ____ most of them will say they are.
   a so that
   b and
   c therefore

3 ____ me you needed money, I would have helped gladly.
   a Had you told
   b Were you telling
   c Should you tell

4 Are you coming to the party – ____ it's still on?
   a assuming
   b were
   c believing

5 ____ a little research and you will find that augmented reality will have a huge impact on learning and many other areas in the future.
   a Had you done
   b Should you do
   c Do

6 ____ harder, you might just pass the test next time.
   a Were you to try
   b Had you tried
   c Should you have tried

7 ____ he come back tomorrow, we'll try to help him.
   a Imagine
   b Should
   c Providing

8 ____ we to consider your offer, when could you start?
   a Were
   b Suppose
   c Should

B Complete the second sentence so that it has a similar meaning to the first sentence. Write three words including the word given. Do not use the word *if* in the second sentence.

1 If you have any queries, you can refer to the briefing document.
   TO
   You could refer to the briefing document ____________ have any queries.

2 If you see Kevin, tell him to call me.
   SHOULD
   ____________ Kevin, tell him to call me.

3 If I'd taken a few more practice tests, I might have passed the exam.
   DONE
   I might have passed the exam ____________ a few more practice tests.

4 Would you have an implant if someone gave you the chance?
   SUPPOSE
   ____________ given the chance, would you have an implant?

5 If they knew it was dangerous, they wouldn't have gone there.
   REALIZED
   ____________ the danger, they wouldn't have gone there.

6 If you ask anyone, they will tell you where to go.
   ASK
   ____________ they will tell you where to go.

VOCABULARY

Science and research; Thinking

A Complete the sentences with the correct form of the words in the box.

conclude	conduct	demonstrate	experiment	finding	hypothesize	norm	participant	speculate

1 We never ________________ any really interesting ________________ in our science lessons, and I think that's why I was never attracted to science as a career.

2 This study clearly ________________ that it's time for a rethink about social ________________ in this country – I think we've been getting it all wrong.

3 We really can't ________________ about what's going to happen – we have no idea!

4 Now that we have gathered the data from both younger and older ________________ in the study, what can we ________________?

5 Scientists often ________________ that things exist long before they can be proven.

6 After we did the research, we arranged a meeting to discuss our ________________ with the development team.

B Choose the correct options to complete the text.

Are you a PROBLEM-SOLVER?

To some people, problem-solving comes naturally. They can [1]***overthink* / *troubleshoot*** a problem by following a logical train of thought, just like a doctor diagnoses an illness. Or in some cases they are instinctively good at understanding how things work, so if they apply themselves to a problem, they will have a [2]***eureka* / *common*** moment sooner or later and get to the bottom of the problem.

To be a practical problem-solver, you need to have a certain amount of [3]***wishful* / *common*** sense. Some people who are great at solving problems are a little [4]***eureka* / *eccentric*** – they behave in strange ways sometimes. Others might be good problem-solvers, but they are really [5]***curious* / *absent***-minded in their daily lives, always forgetting where they left things or failing to finish their sentences when they speak.

So how do you improve your problem-solving skills? Well, it helps if you are [6]***curious* / *eccentric*** about the world – if you're the kind of person who likes to take things apart to see how they work. Also it pays not to [7]***troubleshoot* / *overthink*** a problem – you sometimes need to step away from it and the answer will come to you naturally.

But to a few people, being able to solve complicated problems is just [8]***absent* / *wishful*** thinking – they are never going to be able to do it and if they try, they might end up doing more harm than good!

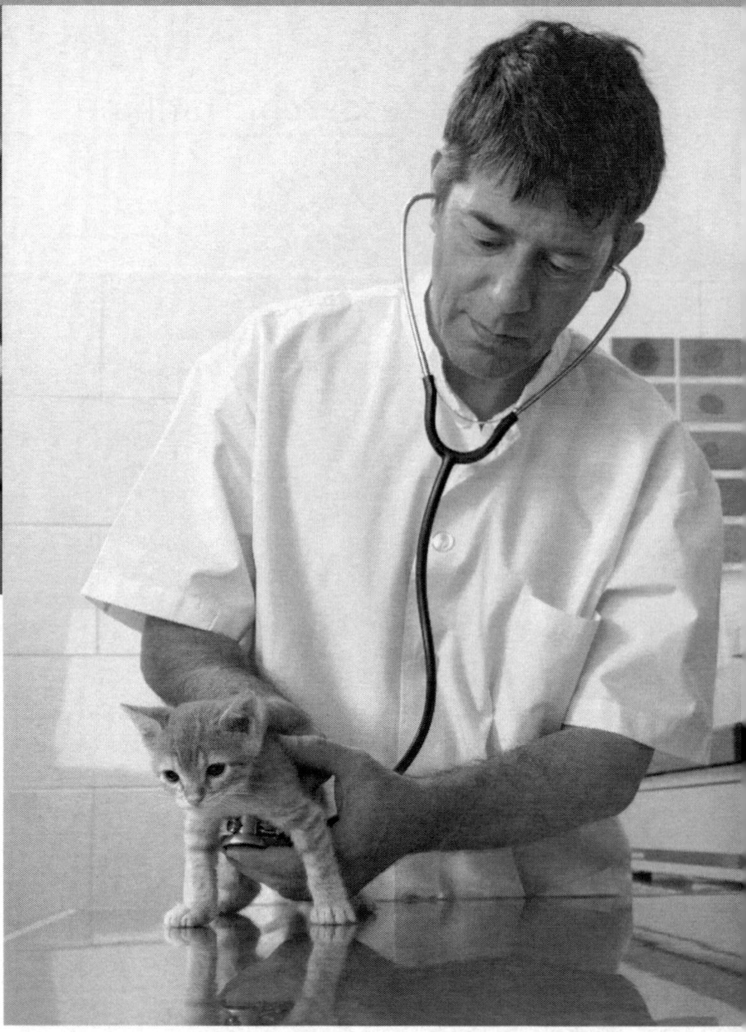

GRAMMAR
Wishes and regrets

A Match the sentences (1–8) to the meanings (a–h).

1 I would love to have been a participant in that study. ___
2 They should have told participants what to expect. ___
3 I wish I could be a participant in that study. ___
4 We should have used more participants. ___
5 If only there were more studies like this. ___
6 I would love to be a participant. ___
7 They should not to have told us what they were doing. ___
8 I wish I wasn't a participant. ___

a I am not a participant.
b There weren't enough participants.
c They explained too much.
d They didn't explain.
e There aren't enough studies.
f I can't be a participant.
g I am a participant.
h I wasn't a participant.

B Complete the sentences with one word in each blank.

1 Tim wishes he ___ been able to study science in college.
2 If only we ___ go anywhere in the world.
3 Claire would love to ___ visited that college.
4 If ___ I knew what job I wanted to do.
5 My brother ___ he was a student again – he would do things differently.
6 Sam ___ have gotten a better certification.
7 If only I ___ more confident.
8 They ___ have studied when they had the chance.

PRONUNCIATION
Adding information or changing the topic

A Look at the underlined words and phrases. Are they used to add information (A) or change the topic (B)?

1 Reading is a good way to keep your mind active. <u>On top of that</u>, books can be a good conversation starter. ___
2 Plus, he also lied about his qualifications. <u>Anyway</u>, we won't get stuck on that – let's move on. ___
3 I'm going to be out of the office from Wednesday onwards. <u>In other words</u>, if you need me, you'll have to catch me on Monday or Tuesday. ___
4 You can, of course, mention this in your essays. <u>By the way</u>, I'm expecting essays next week from all of you. ___
5 I find I process information better if I hear it rather than see it written down. <u>In the same way</u>, I would rather listen to books than read them. ___
6 After that, he was living in Berlin … <u>So</u>, as I was saying, his work is very important for our studies. ___

B Read the sentences in Exercise A aloud, paying attention to the intonation on the underlined sections.

4.2 **C Listen to the sentences from Exercise A. Practice saying the sentences in the same way as the speakers do in the recording.**

4.3 Intelligence

READING

A PREDICT What is intelligence? How would you define intelligence?

B READ FOR GIST Read *What is intelligence?* and *An intelligence test*. Were any of your ideas from Exercise A mentioned?

C READ TO IDENTIFY Match the stylistic features (1–6) to the texts (A or B). Underline in the texts examples of each feature.

1. formal vocabulary ____
2. contractions ____
3. an impersonal style ____
4. complex sentences ____
5. idiomatic language ____
6. short sentences ____

Glossary

contest (v) to disagree
have green fingers (v phr) to be good at growing plants and flowers
sublime (adj) extremely good

D REFLECT Think about the answers to these questions.

1. Have you changed your opinion about what intelligence is? Why/Why not?
2. Do you agree with the conclusions in the articles? Why/Why not?
3. Is there anything in the articles that you want to research further?

A What is intelligence?

Intelligence is one of the most debated subjects in psychology. While there are many competing theories, there is no generally accepted definition. Some believe that it is a single, overall ability, while others believe it comprises a variety of skills, aptitudes and talents. However, despite theoretical differences most agree that how people adapt to their environment is key to understanding intelligence.

Adaptations can occur in numerous situations. It involves making a change in oneself to manage new situations or environments effectively. In certain circumstances, it may mean manipulating the environment itself to suit one's purposes: for example, re-routing a river to irrigate farmland.

Developmental psychologist Howard Gardner in his book *Frames of Mind: The Theory of Multiple Intelligences* (1983) was the first to propose the concept of multiple intelligences. He argued that theories which considered intelligence to be a single, general ability often focused on logical-mathematical intelligence, whereas, the human brain had much wider cognitive abilities.

While many theories of intelligence still accept the notion that intelligence has more than one dimension, the popularity of Gardner's theory among some educators brought criticism on the grounds that its claims cannot be scientifically validated and the criteria Gardner selected are arbitrary (White, 2005).

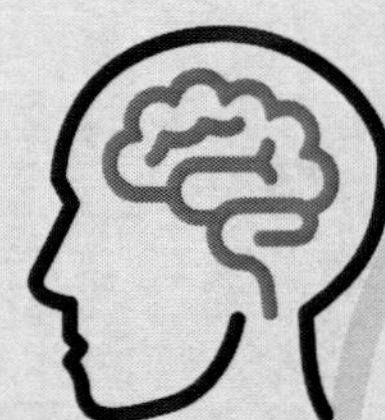

B An intelligence test

I've seen the smartest people do the stupidest things. I once watched, fascinated, as a philosophy major removed a faucet without first turning off the water supply. OK, his degree wasn't in plumbing, but a tiny bit of common sense would have stopped him.

This got me interested in the idea of different types of ability. So I decided to think about where my strengths lie. What are the things that I'm smartest at?

Personally I love being out in nature and cats and dogs seem to like me. But I have to admit, I don't have green fingers. My one attempt to grow an avocado tree failed miserably. OK, maybe I should be looking elsewhere.

Sports? I certainly have developed a little soccer knowledge over the years, but I'm more comfortable on the couch telling you about it than on the soccer field!

Am I a lost cause? Many psychologists now think that how we adapt to new situations is important in measuring how intelligence works. I think what I've realized is that intelligence, at least for me, is less about having a special talent or ability and more about having the right attitude.

LISTENING

A You are going to listen to a discussion about human versus animal intelligence. Which of these abilities do you associate with humans (H), animals (A) or both (B)?

- communicating a complex message ____
- learning from experience ____
- understanding abstract concepts ____
- being able to count ____
- using tools to achieve an objective ____

4.3 **B** **LISTEN FOR GIST** Listen to a discussion about human versus animal intelligence. Did the speakers mention any of the topics from Exercise A?

4.3 **C** **LISTEN FOR MAIN IDEA** Listen again and circle the name of the speaker who mentions these ideas.

1 humans' ability to cope with abstract ideas *Nadia / Charles*
2 the biases of scientists *Nadia / Charles*
3 writing systems *Nadia / Charles*
4 sea creatures communicating with each other *Nadia / Charles*
5 humans lacking certain skills *Nadia / Charles*
6 learning through imitation *Nadia / Charles*

4.4 **D** **RECOGNIZE LOGICAL FALLACIES** Listen to some extracts from the discussion. Are they examples of generalization (A) or anecdotal evidence (B)?

1 ____
2 ____
3 ____

Glossary

accumulation (n) the process by which something (e.g. knowledge) is collected over time
echolocation (n) the biological process used by some animals to navigate
skewed (adj) not accurate because it is affected by somebody's personal opinion

E **REFLECT** Think about the answers to these questions.

1 Which speaker do you agree with more? Why?
2 Which animal do you think is the most intelligent? Why?
3 Which animal is most helpful to humans? Why?
4 What makes us different to animals?
5 What makes us similar to animals?

WRITING

A How important do you think a healthy diet and exercise are for brain function?

B Read the report. Number the paragraphs in the order they should appear and give them the correct paragraph headings from the box below.

Conclusion Discussion Introduction Methods Results

Investigating the effects of diet and exercise on cognitive function

a ________

The group participating in the exercise program performed much better on thinking tests than they had previously. This was seen mainly in executive function: planning, problem-solving and decision-making. The group on the dietary program showed no improvement in executive function. The group on the exercise and diet program showed the greatest improvement in cognitive function, including the speed at which they processed information. All these findings are in line with the original study.

b ________

We strongly believe that in those with age-related cognitive decline, a change in lifestyle involving aerobic exercise and a healthy diet may improve cognitive function. But it can be concluded that more research is needed to confirm this claim.

c ________

Forty adults with an average age of 65 were divided randomly into four groups: 1 Those put on an aerobic exercise program. 2 Those given dietary advice and put on a healthy diet. 3 Those put on a course of both exercise and dietary advice. 4 A control group who didn't alter their dietary or exercise habits at all. Each group stayed on their course for six months.

d ________

This report replicates a study on the effect of diet and exercise on older adults (Behrer, Erikson and Ambrose, 2013). The study suggests that the participants may improve their thinking skills by regular aerobic exercise and good nutrition. This experiment supports the original findings.

e ________

The original researchers found that while there was no proven therapy to halt or reverse age-related cognitive decline, lifestyle changes might delay decline by several years. But the researchers stressed that a larger and more long-term study was needed to confirm their results. Unfortunately the scale of this experiment (much smaller than the original) means it cannot add much to the existing evidence. However, the experiment did produce similar results to the original.

C Read the report again. Find and underline examples of hedging.

Hedging

In a scientific report unless something is a well-established fact, we can use hedging to make our claims less strong and less open to criticism.

1 auxiliary verbs such as *may*, *might* and *could*
2 adverbs such as *probably*, *possibly* and *likely*
3 verbs that allow for some doubt, such as *seem*, *appear*, *suggest*, *indicate*
4 introductory phrases to qualify, such as *We believe*, *We understand*, *In our view*

WRITING PRACTICE

A PREPARE Read about a similar experiment. Imagine you have recently replicated it. Underline anything you think should be included in a report.

In a similar study, 1000 people aged between 60 and 70 were divided into two groups. The study aimed to discover the effect of a program of diet, exercise and brain training on cognitive function. All participants were given the same tests at the beginning of the study and at regular intervals throughout the period. The first group, called the control group, received nothing more than advice. The second group, called the intervention group because the experiment intervened in their behavior, were put on an intensive program of diet, exercise and brain training. At the end of the experiment, the intervention group scored 25% higher than the control group on cognitive function and 83% higher on executive function.

B PLAN You are going to write a report about the experiment. Write notes to help you.

- Use the facts you underlined in Exercise A. You can also use your imagination to come up with information not mentioned in the text.
- Organize your ideas into an appropriate structure for a report, using the paragraph headings from Exercise B.
- Use hedging words/phrases where appropriate.

C WRITE Write your report about the experiment in Exercise A in 220–260 words.

D EDIT Edit your report. Check:

- spelling and punctuation
- the register is formal
- an appropriate structure has been used.

GRAMMAR
The passive voice

A Choose the correct options to complete the sentences.

1. If you make a noise in here, you'll ***have* / *get*** thrown out.
2. Do you remember ***to be* / *being*** introduced to your manager for the first time?
3. At school, we were made ***go* / *to go*** running – even in the snow!
4. The printer was cheap, but the ink needs ***to be* / *being*** changed very frequently.
5. Do you think it's time for me to ***be* / *get*** my hair cut?
6. Is it possible that we're ***been* / *being*** watched through our smartphone cameras?
7. If I'm successful, I'll be ***congratulated* / *congratulating*** by everyone.
8. The office ***had* / *got*** broken into over the weekend.

B Complete the profile with the correct passive form of the verbs in parentheses. Sometimes more than one answer is possible.

Greg Fitzjohn: board game designer

So how did I get my dream job? That's what I [1] ______________ (*always / ask*). Well, the truth is, it happened almost by accident. I [2] ______________ (*invite*) by a college friend who designed board games to spend a few hours in the office with him, just to see what he did. I didn't want to get in the way, so Friday afternoon [3] ______________ (*choose*) – as it's usually a quiet time. It was getting close to five o'clock when my friend's boss burst into the office. I sat quietly listening. The atmosphere was tense. From what I understood, a new game [4] ______________ (*develop*) and a final check needed [5] ______________ (*do*) by Monday. Someone was [6] ______________ (*going to / make*) work over the weekend, but nobody had been found. So I volunteered. The boss dismissed the idea at first, saying things like, 'No, we couldn't. You're not an employee. What if something [7] ______________ (*break*) or lost?' But then she agreed. I took the game home, delivered my report on Monday morning, and on Monday afternoon, I was offered a job!

5.1 Games 21st century games

PRONUNCIATION
Expressing disbelief

A Read the conversations. Underline the words and phrases the second speaker uses to express disbelief.

1 **A:** Well, what does it say on your contract?
B: Contract? What contract?

2 **A:** So, we'd want you to take the game home and, well, just play it as much as possible.
B: Really? Is that all I have to do?

3 **A:** I think they're looking for people to stay late tonight.
B: No way! Again? I'm leaving at the usual time. Not a minute later.

4 **A:** I heard Jones got fired for stealing from his employer.
B: Seriously? After all he's done for the company!

5 **A:** If you hate your job so much, you should leave.
B: Are you joking? Where will I get another job? How will I live?

6 **A:** They say we'll get a bonus if this goes well.
B: Yeah, right! I'm sure *that's* going to happen!

5.1 **B Listen to the conversations. Check your answers to Exercise A.**

C Practice saying the sentences in the same way as the speakers do in the recording in Exercise B.

VOCABULARY
Competition and cooperation

A Match the beginnings of the sentences (1–8) to the endings (a–h).

1 We thought our team would lose but their determination ___
2 To finish the project before the deadline, three of us ___
3 The man who has been accused of the crime is said to be ___
4 The country depends on the support of its ___
5 The complicated rescue operation was ___
6 You win points each time you force your ___
7 Everyone is part of a community, so we think even of our ___
8 In the end, our experience allowed us to ___

a allies in matters of national security.
b collaborated and got the job done quickly.
c opponent into making a mistake.
d cooperating with the police.
e overcome the other team.
f coordinated by the heads of the emergency services.
g prevailed in the end.
h rival players as friends.

B Complete the sentences with the prefix *out* and the correct form of the verbs in the box.

do	number	play	run	smart	weigh

1 The police ________ him – he fell right into their trap.
2 Josh was very competitive and particularly hated being ________ by younger soccer players.
3 Look – I know it's not ideal, but the advantages ________ the disadvantages, so we have no choice.
4 Helen's younger and in better shape than me – I'd never ________ her in a race.
5 Not wanting to be ________ by his neighbor, Clive bought exactly the same car.
6 In my English class, female students ________ males by two to one.

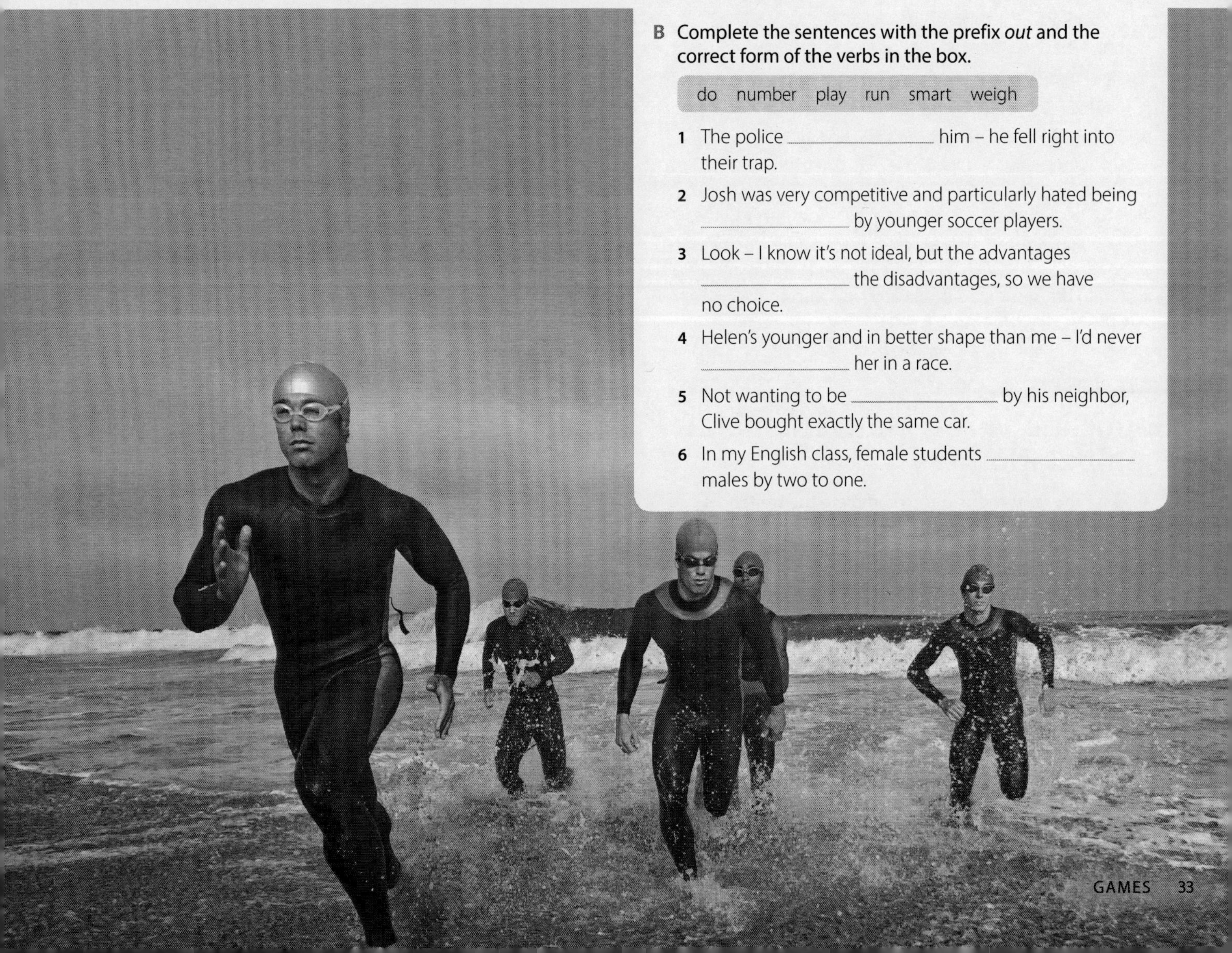

5.2 Games

Serious gaming

PRONUNCIATION

-*ate* words

A Read the sentences aloud. Pay attention to the way you pronounce the underlined words.

1 I don't know if it's appropriate to take flowers or not – these cultural differences are complicated.

2 I find that TV show fascinating – I want to see who gets eliminated next.

3 The estimate for the work was 500 dollars, but that company is not usually very accurate with its initial numbers.

4 If you cooperate fully with the authorities, they can eliminate you as a suspect.

5.2 **B** Listen to the sentences from Exercise A and check the pronunciation.

VOCABULARY

Reporting verbs; Motivation and manipulation

A Choose the correct options to complete the sentences.

1 They *alleged* / *urged* that he had stolen the money but they had no real evidence.

2 You have to *acknowledge* / *imply* that you were wrong.

3 Daniel *instructed* / *asserted* that he was going to lead the team.

4 Fiona *boasted* / *implied* that she was ready to leave the company although she didn't use those words exactly.

5 I *doubt* / *speculate* that anyone can do a better job than Jeanette – she's so good.

6 After losing every match, the manager was forced to *clarify* / *conclude* that his team wasn't very good.

B Complete the text with the words in the box.

act coax inclined nuts spur steer tap

John Murphy
December 5, 2019 at 10:20 am

My company was suffering from a lack of motivation among the staff. We've always tried to [1] ________ into their natural enthusiasm for the job, but there were problems getting teams in different parts of the office to talk and collaborate. Six months ago, we introduced a games room at work and this has really helped. The staff went [2] ________ for Ping-Pong, foosball and board games. We found we no longer had to [3] ________ managers from different teams into attending meetings and company social events. Playing games really [4] ________ them on to cooperate as they became naturally curious about each other's work. Reply

Eloise Waters
December 5, 2019 at 10:48 am

You've highlighted one of the biggest arguments for more opportunities to socialize at work. Staff members are [5] ________ to become demotivated when they don't feel they have shared goals or they feel they are working against other teams. This can make people suspicious and territorial. Then they [6] ________ against the interests of the company and ultimately their own interests. My best advice is to increase opportunities to socialize and play together which gently [7] ________ people toward understanding and trusting their colleagues. Reply

GRAMMAR

Passive reporting structures

A Choose the correct options (a or b) to complete the sentences.

1 He's our longest-serving employee – it can be assumed ___ the truth.
 a to tell
 b that he is telling
2 ___ have employed the services of a professional coach.
 a People rumor that the team
 b The team is rumored to
3 They're easily the best, so ___ to win.
 a they are expected
 b is expected for them
4 The company is said ___ a major investment in the area.
 a to be planning
 b to plan
5 It is widely considered ___ motivation and salary go hand in hand.
 a for
 b that
6 Yes, he is alleged ___ the money, but that hasn't yet been proved.
 a to have stolen
 b he has stolen
7 The robbers ___ armed and extremely dangerous.
 a are known that they are
 b are known to be
8 ___ to be interested in selling off part of the company.
 a It is understood
 b They are understood

B Complete the passive reporting structures with the correct form of the reporting verbs in parentheses.

1 It has ____________ (*report*) the fire broke out in the main building around midnight.
2 It ____________ (*know*) that there are at least two other people involved.
3 Billy ____________ (*understand*) traveling to Spain right now.
4 The escaped prisoner ____________ (*believe*) heading for Brazil.
5 Parachuting from cliffs ____________ (*rumor*) popular in the park.

C Rewrite the sentences so that they start with the words in bold.

1 It's understood that **the exam** has been postponed.
____
2 Everyone knows that **computer simulations** are extremely useful.
____
3 It's thought that **our math professor** is writing a book about Game Theory.
____
4 We expect that **everybody** will vote for the favorite.
____
5 It was alleged that **the other player** had cheated.
____

D Think of ways of completing the following sentences.

- It's expected that …
- It's rumored that …
- It isn't widely known that …
- It's sometimes said that …
- It's believed that …

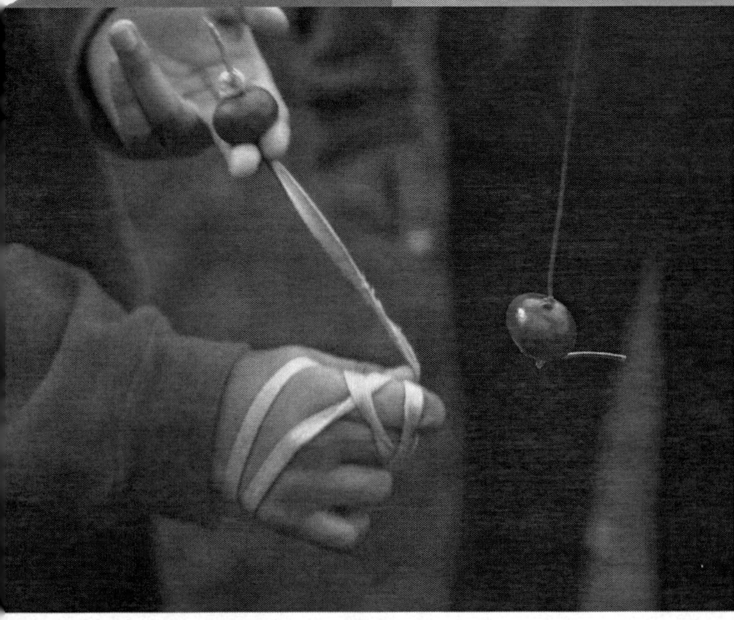

READING

A **PREDICT** Look at the pictures and think about your answers to these questions.

1. Have you played any of these games?
2. Why do you think people play these games?
3. Why do people play games in general?

B **READ FOR GIST** Read *Why we play games*. What different games does the author mention?

C **UNDERSTAND ASIDES** Read the article again and fill in the blanks (1–6) with the asides (a–f).

a I know I do.
b You're impressed, I can tell!
c Well, they would, wouldn't they?
d Go on, admit it!
e Beat that if you can!
f Cheating in other words!

D **READ FOR DETAIL** Read again. Answer the questions.

1. Why do you think the writer tells us the anecdote about the backgammon game?
2. What benefits of team sports are mentioned?
3. What three principal human motives are satisfied by game playing?
4. What factor does the writer think is common to all games?
5. How do games help you get in a state of 'flow'?

Glossary

make-believe (n) the activity of pretending that something is real
pay-off (n) positive result
trance (n) state where you are awake, but not conscious of your surroundings

E **REFLECT** Think about the answers to these questions.

1. Do you think playing video games is a way to escape from reality?
2. In what ways can games prepare people for real-life situations?

WHY WE PLAY GAMES

We are often told that it's the taking part that matters, but if we're being honest, it's winning that really counts. Speaking of which, in a backgammon competition, I once beat the national champion. [1] ___ Well, when I say beat, I mean beat him once in a best-of-five-games match! But for a very short while, I felt like a champion. We're also told sports – particularly team sports – teach us valuable life skills, such as cooperation and fair play. Admirable qualities no doubt, but winning makes you feel a lot better about yourself.

So – just uncomplicated fun and the pleasure of winning? Maybe not. Psychologists claim that it goes much deeper than that. [2] ___ According to Deci and Ryan's self-determination theory, games satisfy a number of important subconscious needs which may not be met in real life. The three main ones are competency, which is our need to feel in control of situations or at least be able to deal with them successfully. Related to this is our desire for autonomy or independence – the feeling that the choices we make are our own. And third, there's what's called relatedness, which is our social instinct – the need to feel important to others in some way and that we are contributing to something larger than ourselves. Work usually fulfills this need in the everyday world.

If that sounds like too much psychology for a simple game of conkers, let's look at some other reasons for our attraction to games. And as we've mentioned conkers, let's use it as an example. For those who don't know, it is a game played by children in the UK where each child has a large nut tied on the end of a piece of string. Most of the fun in playing conkers is in finding ways to strengthen your horse-chestnut

so that it is hard enough to smash your opponent's, but is unbreakable itself, by soaking it in vinegar, for example, or baking it. [3]___ The process sometimes takes days. I can't think of a game that doesn't involve competitiveness. Don't pretend you don't get pleasure from outsmarting an opponent. [4]___

But what, apart from competitiveness, holds our interest? Modern video games offer clear examples of what attracts us to games and keeps us playing, but I think the same features apply, though less obviously, to old-fashioned board games. Many people still enjoy games like Clue – [5]___. These features include a story-telling or make-believe element – often a reflection of the real world – but with more freedom of choice and without real-world consequences. They allow you to act out roles you never would in real life. You have goals and your efforts are rewarded and allow you to measure your progress. Entertainment and escapism with a pay-off. [6]___

Total absorption in games is another aspect of our fascination with them. You reach a state that athletes call being 'in the zone' and psychologists call 'flow'. You are so totally focused and in control that nothing can distract you, and you slip out of time.

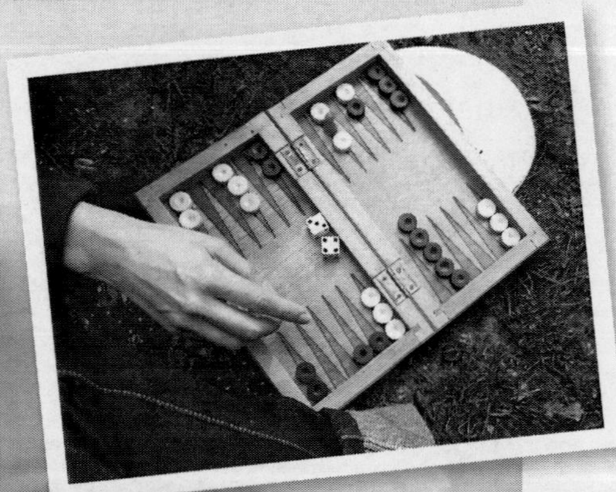

LISTENING

A Work in pairs. Look at the picture of the video gamer. What might be some problems with this activity?

B 5.3 **LISTEN FOR MAIN IDEA** Listen to the podcast. Check (✓) only the things that are true according to Andrea.

1. If somebody becomes less social, it can be a warning that there is a problem. ☐
2. Games are the main reason people get addicted to the internet. ☐
3. Governments have solved the problem by passing laws restricting screen time. ☐
4. The problem isn't limited to younger users. ☐
5. Many gamers feel more at home in an artificial community. ☐
6. Gaming encourages people to do more physical activity. ☐

C 5.3 **LISTEN FOR SOLUTIONS** Listen again and choose the correct options (a, b or c) to complete the sentences.

1. According to Andrea, gamers
   - **a** need to be banned from playing games by law.
   - **b** should be supported to set boundaries themselves.
   - **c** should be stopped from playing by their parents.
2. Andrea thinks the deeper cause of the problem is
   - **a** our desire for rewards and community.
   - **b** social networks refusing to be positive role models for gamers.
   - **c** the gamer's determination to play games.
3. The problem can be solved
   - **a** by recognizing the causes and supporting the gamer.
   - **b** by encouraging them to adopt a different persona.
   - **c** by governments and parents working together to make gamers do more physical activity.

Glossary

persona (n) particular personality or character – often different to the one you normally have

D **REFLECT** Which solution do you believe would be most effective in tackling problems with video gaming?

WRITING

A Read the report and answer the questions.

1 Which company is the report for?
2 What is the purpose of the report?
3 Which company had some dissatisfied staff?

B USING DEPERSONALIZATION Rewrite the sentences/clauses (a–e) in formal, depersonalized language. Then use them to fill in the blanks (1–5) in the report. More than one answer is sometimes possible.

a They observed higher levels of motivation in both staff and customers,
Higher levels ______________________,

b An app on the staff's smartphones records all the activities they perform and turns them into points.
All activities ______________________.

c … we decided we should conduct an investigation …
… it ______________________ …

d I should mention, however, that an app such as the one *GetFit* uses …
It ______________________

e They have also introduced incentives for those doing work such as cleaning.
Incentives ______________________.

WRITING PRACTICE

A PREPARE Read the task below and write notes.
You have been asked by the manager of the sports equipment company you work for to write a report about using games to attract customers to your company's exhibit space at a trade fair. Think about how traditional games (bingo, spin the wheel, etc), apps and virtual reality may help draw customers to your exhibit space.

B PLAN You are going to write a report for the task in Exercise A.

- Organize your notes into an appropriate structure for a report.
- Use formal, depersonalized language.
- Give your recommendations in the final paragraph.

C WRITE Write your report in 200–300 words. Use your plan to help you.

Using games to improve motivation and efficiency at *Sports Unlimited*

Background

At a recent meeting of the Board of Directors of *Sports Unlimited*, [1] ______________ into similar businesses where gamification has been introduced to improve staff motivation and efficiency. This report summarizes the research and offers some recommendations to the Board.

Case study 1: GetFit

This company's use of gamification is well known. [2] ______________ When a certain level is reached, the user is rewarded, either with a bonus or a company perk, such as a day off. The app has been made available to customers as well and has proved to be highly popular. [3] ______________ but more so in the latter. However, some staff were worried about losing their privacy.

Case study 2: World Sports Inc.

Here gamification has been introduced not only to increase motivation but as a training tool. Staff are encouraged to adopt different roles within the company via an app that sets them tasks appropriate to that position. This provides a deeper knowledge of all aspects of the business and encourages staff to think about their future in the company. Since its introduction, there has been a 25% increase in efficiency. [4] ______________ As with *GetFit*, it is a points/rewards system and has increased motivation for people engaged in these tasks.

Recommendations

For our purposes here at *Sports Unlimited*, I would recommend an app similar to that used by *World Sports Inc.*, or one very like it, as the most suitable for in-house use, which would not be too expensive to install. [5] ______________ but for customer use only, would help increase brand awareness. Finally, it should be noted that some form of a points/rewards game is always a good motivator.

6.1 Discoveries

Challenging journeys

VOCABULARY

Journeys and adventures; Three-part phrasal verbs

A Complete the text with the words in the box.

beaten embarked globetrotters heart impenetrable long-haul provisions uncharted

Around the globe in 80 days

Around the globe in 80 days? Well the 19th-century journalist Nellie Bly did it in 72 days. But role models for intrepid female adventurers aren't confined to history books. The image of 19th-century explorers fighting their way through ¹_______________ terrain and large expeditions into dangerous and ²_______________ territories is being replaced by solo modern-day adventurers and ³_______________.

Anna McNuff ⁴_______________ on a seven-month cycle ride into the ⁵_______________ of the US. She crossed every state, traveling 11,000 miles on a pink bike. She had to deal with the various challenges, including weather (cold, wind, floods and blizzards) and wild animals. In 2015, she ditched the bike and ran about 1,900 miles to complete the Te Araroa Trail in New Zealand. While water wasn't a problem, she sometimes had to carry essential ⁶_______________ (like chocolate!) to last for up to seven days.

While we can certainly learn from the spirit of past adventurers who endured difficult conditions to explore their world, we shouldn't forget modern-day female role models and the amazing adventures that are being had right now. And with the advent of more affordable ⁷_______________ flights, getting off the ⁸_______________ track is more possible than ever.

B Complete the sentences with one word in each blank.

1 I need a vacation to help me switch _______________ from work for a while.

2 I'm playing tennis tomorrow morning at eight o'clock. Are you up _______________ it?

3 Carol is always talking about cleaning up her desk, but she never seems to get _______________ to it.

4 If you come up _______________ any problems, just call me.

5 When you look _______________ on your schooldays, do you think of them as a happy time?

6 Nobody found _______________ about the missing money until the thief had left the country.

7 The best way to brush _______________ on your French is to spend some time in France.

8 The problem with having a cell phone and a computer at home is that there's no getting away _______________ work.

GRAMMAR
Past modals of speculation and deduction

A **Choose the correct options to complete the sentences.**

1 He *can't* / *mustn't* have been serious about leaving – he loves it here.
2 She *must* / *might* have mentioned it, but I really don't remember.
3 It's highly *likely* / *distinct* that the bad weather contributed to the accident.
4 Sandra *may have decided* / *may decided* to turn back because of the snow on the road.
5 Some people say the pyramids must *had* / *have* been built using very advanced technology.
6 There's a distinct *probability* / *possibility* that the explorer died of some kind of disease.
7 You *could* / *must* have seen that movie – everyone knows it!
8 He *may well* / *well may* have called me – I've had my phone turned off all morning.

B **Complete the second sentence so that it has a similar meaning to the first sentence. Use three words including the word given in bold.**

1 There's a good chance he has decided not to come because of the weather.
WELL
He ______ decided not to come because of the weather.

2 I think he probably changed his mind about applying for the job.
EXTREMELY
It's ______ he changed his mind about applying for the job.

3 I'm sure they got out of the building.
LEFT
They ______ the building safely.

4 It's possible that Andrea forgot where we live.
MIGHT
Andrea ______ where we live.

5 It's very likely that he fell asleep.
DISTINCT
There's ______ that he fell asleep.

6 I'm certain it wasn't me who called you. I would remember.
CAN'T
I would remember calling you, so it ______ me.

PRONUNCIATION
Showing your attitude

A **Read the sentences aloud, paying attention to the way you pronounce the underlined phrases.**

1 Well, in general, I agree with most of the changes to our contracts, but the question is, can we afford to live on the wages they're offering?
2 Allegedly, he got the job because his father is friends with the manager. The main thing is, he is pretty good at it, so that might just be a rumor.
3 Supposedly, the money's going to come from the sale of one of the smaller companies – the question is, which one?
4 On the whole, I think the project has been successful. Surely, management must be pleased with it.

6.1 **B** **Listen to the sentences from Exercise A. Practice saying the sentences in the same way as the speakers do in the recording.**

GRAMMAR

-ing and infinitive forms

A Complete the text with the correct form of the verbs in parentheses.

Finding sources you can trust

For the curious mind (and for those minds paid to be curious), the internet is an amazing tool. Researchers and journalists have access to stories across business, politics and humor. And the public has gotten used to [1]______________ (*read*) online. But in some cases, fake stories are circulated on purpose.

It's just so easy [2]______________ (*spread*) a story these days – whether it's true or false. Before the internet, most news came via newspapers which had a reputation [3]______________ (*maintain*), so they would at least take care not [4]______________ (*do*) too much that damaged their credibility. But now, with both the speed at which stories are being written and shared and the ease with which fake news can be spread online, we may have difficulty [5]______________ (*tell*) the difference between credible and questionable news.

B Match the beginnings of the sentences (1–6) to the endings (a–f).

1 When I have guests, I always worry that there's not enough food ___
2 I don't think you'll get into trouble for ___
3 Is this a good time ___
4 Have fun ___
5 There are a lot of online resources ___
6 In your opinion, is there any point ___

a surfing, but don't take any risks.
b to help you.
c to go around.
d being five minutes late.
e to talk to you about my essay?
f waiting to see the manager today?

C Choose the option which is closest in meaning to the sentence.

1 They stopped to analyze the data.
   a They were analyzing data, then stopped.
   b They were doing something else, then started analyzing data.
2 She remembered to heat the liquid.
   a She remembered something she needed to do.
   b She had the memory of doing something.

VOCABULARY
Binomial expressions

A Complete the binomial expressions with the words in the box. There are three extra words that you do not need to use.

away by greet order quiet soul sound take tear there tidy

1 When we go to the country, we like to sit and enjoy the peace and __________.
2 __________ and large, my job gives me everything I need.
3 Every relationship needs a little give and __________.
4 The boss always comes early to meet and __________ people when there's an event.
5 That was far and __________ the best movie I've ever seen!
6 The job of the police is to uphold law and __________.
7 Keeping the work area clean and __________ is a matter of safety, too.
8 There's a little wear and __________, but you'd expect that on a ten-year-old car.

B Complete the binomial expressions with two words in each blank.

1 We searched far __________ for the phone, but it was gone.
2 His is a real rags-__________ story – they weren't rich as children.
3 When he plays soccer, he really puts his heart __________ into the game.
4 Time __________, they get the work wrong, even after I've shown them.
5 Frank had worked two shifts back __________ so he was exhausted.
6 It didn't happen right away. Slowly __________, I got used to living here though.
7 We watched a grandfather and grandson walk side __________ down the lane.
8 Why is she getting so upset? It's not a life-__________ situation – she's just deciding which outfit to wear!

PRONUNCIATION
Pauses and pitch in presentations

A Read the beginning of a presentation and mark a (/) in red where you would take a pause. Also think about where you would step up to a higher pitch to start a new topic or step down to a lower pitch to end a topic.

I'd like to talk to you today about the bad side of staying informed. I don't mean for one minute to suggest that you should stay uninformed – it's good to keep up-to-date with what's happening – but too much news causes us stress, and that's official! Studies suggest that many of us check headlines on an hourly basis, and now experts are telling us that's not good for our state of mind, our sleep patterns or even our relationships. One of the biggest dangers is that the news, in order to hold our attention, has to be shocking. Now, I like to see an action or a horror movie occasionally, but imagine that level of tension *all* the time. Our nerves just wouldn't take it. And yet that's just what happens when we are constantly plugged in to continuous news stories. The least we should do is to make sure we don't watch the news just before going to bed. At least that might help us to sleep better at night, which in turn will help us cope with everything else.

6.2 **B Listen to someone reading the text from Exercise A. Does the speaker pause and change pitch in the same places as you? Now practice reading the presentation with the same pauses and pitch changes as the speaker in the recording.**

READING

A PREDICT Look at the pictures and the title of the article. What information will the article include? What questions will it answer?

B Read *Mungo Park: the last adventure*. Were your predictions in Exercise A correct?

C READ FOR DETAIL Read the article again and answer the questions.

1. Why was Mungo Park chosen to lead his first expedition to Africa?
2. Which two things caused him to abandon his first expedition?
3. What can we understand about Park's personality from his communication with home?
4. What happened to the people who went looking for Mungo Park?

D REFLECT Think about the answers to these questions.

1. What makes people undertake dangerous expeditions?
2. What motivates modern-day explorers to follow in the footsteps of older explorers?

Mungo Park: THE LAST ADVENTURE

MUNGO PARK.

Mungo Park was a young Scottish explorer who went in search of the Niger River in West Africa. After training to be a surgeon, he traveled to South-East Asia as a ship's medical officer. While in the region, he studied the plant and animal life of Sumatra and, on his return, described several new species of fish and plants that he had recorded. This gained him a certain amount of recognition and, when the African Association was looking for someone to head an expedition to explore the course of the Niger River, Park was an obvious choice.

His first African expedition therefore began in 1795 and Park followed the Gambia River for 200 miles (about 320 km), entering into unknown territory as he encountered the Senegal River. He was then taken prisoner for four months before escaping and eventually reaching his target, the Niger River. Lack of supplies meant that he was only able to follow it for 80 miles (about 128 km) and, on turning back, he became seriously ill. When he finally made it back to Britain in 1797, he wrote *Travels in the Interior Districts of Africa*, which was popular and helped to further his reputation.

In 1805, he was commissioned for a second expedition to chart the course of the Niger River. This expedition was dogged by misfortune from the start. Forty men set off from the Gambia in the rainy season – the worst time to do so. By the time they reached the Niger, only 11 men remained alive. However, Park made no mention of these tragic events in the letters which he sent home. He was determined to complete the expedition and set off from Bamako along the unmapped stretch of the Niger.

Eventually, a party was sent to find out what could have happened to Park and his men. Isaaco, a local guide, was hired to help them. Given that they had set out in the rainy season, might their canoes have been caught in rapids and overturned or broken against rocks and the men drowned? Had they run out of provisions? Despite being well-armed, could they have been attacked and overcome by a hostile tribe? Or could they have died of disease or been the prey of wild animals? Although death was the most likely outcome, and with no trace of Park, there were still many rumors back in Britain claiming that he had survived.

Isaaco managed to find a man named Amadi, one of Park's guides, who gave his account of events. They had been attacked several times by men in canoes and they had, as expected, encountered dangerous rapids, which they survived until they reached the rapids at Bussa where the river narrows. There, they were caught on a rock and attacked by hostile tribesmen who had been waiting in ambush. The odds against them were too high; the story goes that Park jumped into the river and it is assumed that he drowned. Amadi was taken prisoner.

In 1827, hopeful that his father might still be alive, Mungo Park's son, Thomas, set off to Africa in search of him. Within a month, however, all contact with him was lost. Stories circulated that he had died of fever but his body was never recovered. As recently as 2003, a man named Christian Velten set out on a six-month expedition following in the footsteps of Mungo Park. After a short time, contact with him was also lost.

Glossary

ambush (n) a surprise attack by people in a concealed place
be dogged by (v phr) to have problems/difficulties over a long period of time
rapids (n pl) a steep, rocky place in a river with a fast current

LISTENING

A PREDICT What logistical problems do you think 19th-century explorers faced? Think about:

- transportation
- communication
- provisions
- technology.

6.3 **B LISTEN FOR MAIN IDEA** Listen to the first part of a podcast about two Antarctic expeditions and answer the questions.

1 What were the names of the two explorers?

____

2 What was their goal?

____

3 When did these events take place?

____

4 What was the result of the expeditions?

____

6.4 **C** Listen to the rest of the recording. Check (✓) the topics mentioned.

- [ ] Communication
- [ ] Finances
- [ ] Friendship
- [ ] Food and nutrition
- [ ] Goals
- [ ] Historical background
- [ ] Mountaineering
- [ ] Route planning
- [ ] Transportation

6.5 **D LISTEN TO WRITE NOTES** Listen to the whole podcast. Write notes on the following questions.

1 Why Antarctica?	
2 What was life like for the explorers?	
3 What equipment was needed?	
4 How did Scott and Amundsen's goals differ?	
5 What means of transportation did Scott use?	
6 What was wrong with his choices?	
7 How did Amundsen plan his route?	
8 What was wrong with Scott's preparations?	

Glossary

depot (n) place where things are stored
hardship (n) situation in which life is very difficult
rations (n pl) restricted amounts of food for people such as soldiers

E REFLECT Does this story remind you of any other similar adventures you have read or heard about?

WRITING

A Look at the picture and the essay question below. How do you think the picture might be related to the content of this essay?

What are the benefits of discovering new species?

B Complete the essay by matching these missing topic sentences (1–5) to the paragraphs (a–e).

1. Penicillin was produced from a fungus.
2. If you thought there was nothing new under the sun, then think again.
3. Clearly, there is still much to learn about the surface of the planet we inhabit.
4. Each life form has a special role in the ecosystem.
5. 'Biomimicry' is the science of copying nature's adaptations and applying them to technology.

The benefits of discovering NEW SPECIES

a___ And new species may provide further breakthroughs in medicine. For example, extracts from a newly discovered plant, *Kindia gangan*, a member of the coffee family, suggest that it may have medical applications.

b___ The gecko's ability to stick to walls and ceilings, the silk with which spiders spin their webs and the way butterfly wings react to light have all been exploited in technological innovations. Discoveries of new species may well lead to other innovations in the future.

c___ Biologists estimate that the vast majority of life on Earth – between 3 and 100 million species – remains undiscovered. There are three enormous benefits to discovering new species: each new life form helps us understand more about biodiversity, may prove a valuable source of new medicines or could inspire new technology.

d___ The benefits of continuing to discover new plants, insects and micro-organisms are enormous. They will help us treat the planet with greater knowledge and respect, with more informed conservation strategies. They can provide us with new medicines, possibly even for diseases we think incurable. Also, the weird and wonderful adaptations plants and creatures make to survive in their environments provide the inspiration for technologies that benefit us all.

e___ Biodiversity is the way in which all these life forms function together to maintain a balance. As we discover new species, the better we understand how these systems work, which will help us implement more effective conservation strategies for threatened ecosystems such as coral reefs.

C STRUCTURING AN EXPOSITORY ESSAY Put the paragraphs (a–e) in the correct order (1–5).

1. introduction ___
2. first benefit ___
3. second benefit ___
4. third benefit ___
5. conclusion ___

WRITING PRACTICE

A PREPARE Read the essay question below. Use the questions 1–5 to write notes for the essay.

What are the benefits of foreign travel?

1. Have you ever traveled to another country? If not, would you like to?
2. What did/could you learn by visiting another country?
3. What did/could you learn about yourself?
4. Can traveling abroad teach you more about your own country?
5. Make a list of the benefits of travel.

B PLAN You are going to write an expository essay for the task in Exercise A.

- Organize your notes into an appropriate structure for an expository essay.
- Use a topic sentence to introduce each main paragraph.
- Finish with a conclusion that summarizes the points you made in the main body of the essay in the same order.

C WRITE Write your essay in 220–260 words.

GRAMMAR
it clefting

A Write one word in each blank to complete the sentences.

1 It ______ you who caused the problem; it was me.
2 It was the long ocean journey ______ put me off the idea.
3 The problem wasn't her lack of qualifications – ______ was her personality.
4 The money's OK, but ______ the hours that I don't like.
5 It was ______ visit my parents that I last went home.
6 It was my brother ______ persuaded me to go to college.
7 It was ______ I had to pay for something that I realized my wallet was missing.
8 It wasn't until we got home ______ we realized how close we had come to disaster.

B Rewrite the sentences using *it* clefting to draw attention to the underlined words or phrases.

1 I applied to run the race <u>to raise money for charity</u>.
______
2 <u>The physical challenge</u> isn't a problem for me; <u>the psychological challenge</u> is!
______
3 I've only noticed the pain in my legs <u>now</u>, <u>after I've been running for five days</u>.
______
4 <u>My sister</u> persuaded me to enter the race.
______
5 I didn't run <u>a marathon</u> – I ran <u>an ultramarathon</u>!
______

C Rewrite the sentences beginning with *It*. Sometimes more than one answer is possible.

1 They really wanted to see the landscape paintings.
______
2 He was to blame for breaking the window, not her.
______
3 The part Steven didn't understand was at the end.
______
4 I'm talking to you!
______
5 What bothers me is the cost.
______
6 Eliza said 'no' because she was scared.
______
7 You only really appreciate something when it's gone.
______
8 I didn't realize how dangerous it was until I got back.
______

D Complete the sentences so that they are true for you.

1 It wasn't only ______ it was ______.
2 It was my ______ who ______ me to ______.
3 It was because ______ that I ______.
4 It was to ______ that I ______ not to ______.

VOCABULARY
Feelings

A Chose the correct options to complete the text.

In touch with your FEELINGS?

A lot of the time, we do not have control over our emotions because they are instinctive reactions in response to a particular set of circumstances.

This is often useful – for example, when we are [1]***indifferent / disgusted*** by the sight of something, such as rotten food, it may well mean that we should stay away from it to be safe. Some people, however, sometimes try to stay in control of their emotions. They may want to appear tough or [2]***frustrated / resilient***. But sometimes these people can seem arrogant or [3]***superior / hysterical***.

However, there are times when we need to be a little [4]***humble / disgusted*** and accept that it is not always in our power to control how we feel. We should accept that it is natural to be [5]***devastated / humble*** when something awful happens.

But we should still strive to be [6]***grumpy / courageous*** even when we are frightened and to deal with things in a calm manner. At times like these, it really is possible to control our emotions.

7.1 Extremes

Beyond the limits

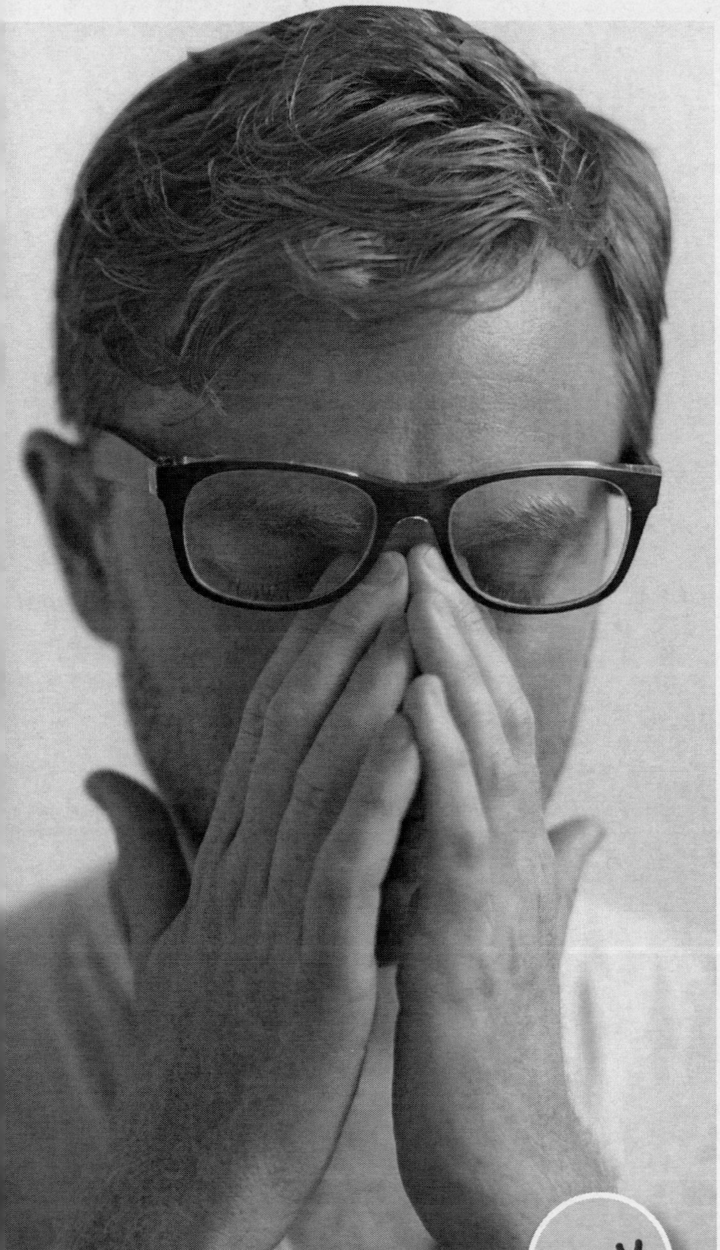

B Complete the sentences with words from Exercise A. Sometimes more than one answer is possible.

1 Jack was very __________ and kept calm up until the last moment.

2 Emma is a very __________ person who never likes to talk about her achievements.

3 When we saw the extent of the damage, we were __________.

4 The BASE jumpers were left feeling __________ after their jump was canceled three times due to high winds.

5 Carla seems almost __________ to fear – however terrifying the situation, she always looks calm.

6 Nigel thinks he's better than everyone and he always acts in a(n) __________ manner.

7 Stop being horrible to everyone! I think the reason you're so __________ this morning is that you went to bed so late last night.

8 Alex was __________ – he just kept screaming and crying.

PRONUNCIATION
Intonation in question tags

A Look at the question tags and draw arrows to show whether they should have rising (↗) or falling (↘) intonation.

1 It's ridiculous, isn't it? ___

2 Let's meet over the weekend, shall we? ___

3 We couldn't make it next weekend, could we? ___

4 Wow, that's good. You know what you're doing, don't you? ___

5 It's cold today, isn't it? ___

6 You couldn't help me out here, could you? ___

7.1 **B Listen to the sentences from Exercise A and check your answers.**

C Practice saying the sentences in the same way as the speakers do in the recording in Exercise B.

7.2 Extremes

Extreme jobs

VOCABULARY

Polysemy; Intensifiers

A Complete the text with the words in the box.

application   competition   conditions   land   pressure   sick

A life in CYBERCRIME

When I left school, my number one priority was to [1] ______________ a well-paid job. I didn't care what. All I knew was that I was [2] ______________ of studying and I wanted to use my computer skills.

I knew there was a lot of [3] ______________ in the job market, especially for IT jobs – I had heard crazy numbers, like 500 people applying for one job. I felt a great deal of [4] ______________ on me to get a job and the longer I stayed unemployed, the greater it became.

Almost a decade later and I am still amazed that I am now a legal computer hacker. That's right, I work for a security company and use my computer skills to make companies safer against cybercrime.

A very impressive [5] ______________ got me my first interview with my current employer and after two more I was finally successful!

There were a few strange [6] ______________ in the contract, and I have to be very cautious about personal data and intellectual property, but the money is very good.

B Rearrange the letters to make intensifiers.

1 Paul was **miymelnse** ______________ proud of his success in the competition.

2 It's **tuetyrl** ______________ ridiculous to expect your parents to support you when you're in your 20s.

3 I'm not **lgtoeharte** ______________ sure I trust him.

4 Jane was **ayntcoiebl** ______________ different after her trip to India.

5 It's **yetlairvel** ______________ easy to get a job with that company – they're desperate for staff.

6 Georgia did **krrebmyaal** ______________ well in her exams.

7 You can't call it 'his version of the truth'; it was an **utrogiht** ______________ lie.

8 Things changed **ciradlyal** ______________ once the new management team took over.

9 It's **capryalctil** ______________ impossible to get a transfer to another branch – they almost never allow it.

10 Yeah, I think Philip was **tsohemwa** ______________ confused – he had a strange look on his face!

GRAMMAR
what clefting and *all* clefting

A Find and correct the mistakes in the sentences.

1 What that happened was I got confused.

____

2 Why crashed the computer I have no idea!

____

3 Pets are easy – they all need is food, water and some attention.

____

4 That Lara likes about summer is being able to relax on the balcony.

____

5 You all need is a snack and some good company!

____

6 What's that Simon can't stand about this job – the silly rules!

____

7 That we ended up doing was taking the train.

____

8 I didn't have my phone on me so what did I do was ask a colleague to borrow hers.

____

B Rewrite the sentences using the words in parentheses.

1 In the end they turned back. (*what*)

____

2 We don't need anything except a map. (*all*)

____

3 I can't stand sleeping in a tent. (*what*)

____

4 Rex loves playing with his ball in the yard. (*what*)

____

5 They needed a drink of water. (*all*)

____

6 You need a vacation. (*what*)

____

7 Tanya wanted to be a ballerina more than anything. (*what*)

____

8 She's just asking for a short break. (*all*)

____

C Complete the second sentence so that it has a similar meaning to the first sentence. Write between two and five words, including the word given.

1 She loves basketball because she gets to meet up with her friends – that's what she loves most.

WHAT

_______________ basketball is that she gets to meet up with her friends.

2 She only wants a little bit of consideration, nothing else.

ALL

_______________ little bit of consideration, nothing else.

3 He didn't know what to do so he called his dad.

DID

He didn't know what to do so _______________ his dad.

4 I like camping, except for the insects. I hate dealing with them.

STAND

_______________ camping is dealing with insects.

5 I've realized something about my job – it doesn't take a genius to do it!

WHAT

_______________ that it doesn't take a genius to do my job!

6 My sister doesn't remember much about her first school – just playing outside.

ALL

_______________ about her first school is playing outside.

PRONUNCIATION
any and *really*

A Underline *really* and *any* in these sentences when they are stressed.

1 The movie was really amazing, actually – we loved it!
2 I don't want any old doctor – I want the one I always see.
3 The questions they asked me were really ridiculous!
4 Any questions you have will be answered at the end, OK?
5 Well, you don't tell your password to just anybody.
6 Let's go – anywhere's better than here!
7 The test was really hard but he thinks he passed.
8 'Which movie do you want to watch?'
'Oh, any one. You choose.'

7.2 **B Listen to the sentences from Exercise A.**

C Practice saying the sentences in the same way as the speakers do in the recording.

Surf's up

READING

A PREDICT Look at the picture and think about these questions.

1 What are some of the dangers involved in surfing?

2 What is it about this sport that appeals to people?

B READ FOR GIST Read *Surf's up* and answer the questions.

1 What is the main danger for surfers?

2 What claim do surfers make about the appeal of their sport?

3 What impression do non-surfers have of the surfing life?

4 As a profession, does surfing pay well?

C Complete the article with the reference devices in the box.

it it's many one such incidents that (x2) those who which you

D READ FOR REFERENCES What do the reference devices in Exercise C refer to? Decide if they are anaphoric: referring back (A), cataphoric: referring forward (C) or exophoric: referring outside the text (E).

1 ___ 3 ___ 5 ___ 7 ___ 9 ___

2 ___ 4 ___ 6 ___ 8 ___ 10 ___

Glossary

endorsement (n) support given by a well-known person to products as a form of advertising

riptide (n) a strong surface current from the shore out to sea

sponsorship (n) support from an organization that promotes sporting or artistic activity

trajectory (n) path, direction of a moving object

E REFLECT Think about the answers to these questions.

1 Why do we sometimes like to be scared?

2 Would you like to earn your living from doing an extreme sport? Why/Why not?

[1]________ may look like fun in the sun, but for some surfing is a job, a full-time occupation. Also a passion. And there is money to be made – if you're good enough. I'll come back to that later. But before [2]________ get on your board, and paddle out to where the waves break, you should be aware of some of the dangers involved in surfing – or just being in the ocean.

Shark attacks are everyone's fear, surfer or not, but they are not as frequent a cause of injury or death as other factors; though [3]________ do get a lot of media coverage. Waves are powerful forces of nature and a wipeout, or being thrown off your board, can cause serious injuries. Your board, too, becomes a danger in such incidents, as it is sent spinning into the air and you have no idea where it will land. You just hope it doesn't hit you, especially with the pointy end. Now you're struggling in rough water, there are riptides to worry about, which are usually present at good surfing areas. [4]________ takes us to the most obvious danger – drowning. So why take it up, let alone make it your profession?

The excitement, of course. Even with a small wave, say one meter high, you experience the awesome power of nature – and you're going with it. Riding [5]________ taller than yourself, the experience is even greater. [6]________ claim there's no better sensual experience in the world. There's nothing but the wave, your board and your body – all your senses fully engaged: the sound of the surf, the taste of salt, the colors and the sensation of speed. The slightest shift in weight will alter your trajectory in the direction you want to go, or send you crashing into the surf. And no two waves are ever the same. An extreme challenge, then, but one that brings great pleasure. Imagine what it would be like to catch a wave as tall as a tower. For some, [7]________ is their speciality; but I assume they must be inhumanly confident or mad!

For [8]________ are just onlookers, the lifestyle, too, has its attractions. What could be better than a job that takes you all over the world to exotic places, spending your days on beaches? It sounds like a permanent vacation. But [9]________ not all travel and parties. Like anything worth doing, it takes hard work, ambition and time. I mentioned earlier that there was money to be made, but it's not great. There's no real job security, like a salary, health insurance, pension or paid leave. Top surfers get money from winning competitions, and a lot of that goes toward traveling to the next competition. It's a sport and like, say, tennis, those at the top get the big money, while the rest fight it out for smaller and smaller amounts. Apart from [10]________, once a surfer has made a name for himself or herself, there's money to be made from sponsorships and endorsements.

LISTENING

A PREDICT What personal qualities do you think a performer would need to be a successful tightrope walker?

7.3 **B LISTEN FOR SPECIFIC INFORMATION** Listen to a program about tightrope walking. Complete the texts with a word or short phrase in each blank.

Nik Wallenda

The famous tightrope walker comes from a family of [1]________________ performers going back generations. His great-grandfather died in [2]________________ trying to walk between two buildings. His most famous stunt, walking across the Niagara Falls, attracted [3]________________ viewers.

Philippe Petit

A [4]________________ movie about his achievement called *Man on Wire* was released in 2008. He found fame after walking a tightrope between two skyscrapers in [5]________________ City for a distance of [6]________________ meters. The event was organized [7]________________ because it was illegal. A [8]________________ were used to fire a guiding rope across the space.

7.3 **C LISTEN FOR CAUSATION** Listen again and choose the correct options (a, b or c) to answer the questions or complete the sentences.

1 What is the key factor behind Nik Wallenda's successful career as a tightrope walker?
   - **a** Pressure from his family
   - **b** The achievements of his great-grandfather
   - **c** His desire for publicity

2 He attracts audiences of millions because
   - **a** he walked across the Niagara Falls.
   - **b** they think he has a lot of charisma.
   - **c** he knows how to successfully exploit the media.

3 Many people became interested in Philippe Petit again because
   - **a** his exploits are illegal.
   - **b** his most famous walk involved New York's Twin Towers.
   - **c** of a movie which featured his most famous achievement.

4 What was the immediate result of Philippe Petit's walk between the Twin Towers?
   - **a** The New York police arrested him.
   - **b** He became famous overnight.
   - **c** A movie was made about his exploits.

Glossary

feat (n) an impressive and often dangerous act
heist (n) an organized robbery (of a bank, jewelry store, etc)

D REFLECT Think about the answers to these questions.

1 Do you think that the people you heard about in the recording are courageous or foolish?

2 Why do people enjoy watching such terrifying stunts?

Tree Surgeon – Montana

The US Forest Service is recruiting an arborist/ tree surgeon. The job involves collecting data, assessing tree health and treatment, assessing hazards posed by trees, pruning and removing branches and planting and felling trees.

A certificate in Forest Management is not essential, but some experience in woodland ecology and conservation or arboriculture would be valuable. We are looking for an experienced climber skilled in the use and maintenance of power tools. The candidate must be prepared to work outdoors in all conditions, be able to work at heights, remain calm in tense situations, follow instructions in detail and work well as a member of a team.

Applications to: Henry Swaffer, US Forest Service.

Dear Mr. Swaffer,

I am writing to apply for the position of tree surgeon at the US Forest Service.

You will see on my résumé (attached) that I have a certificate in arboriculture and experience in woodland conservation as a volunteer for the American Forest Foundation, where I [1]was in charge of a team [2]whose task was to collect data about the health and growth of trees. This work provided me with valuable insights into woodland preservation.

Later, I [3]became the manager of a small tree surgery company where I [4]had responsibility for the care and maintenance of woodland in the Bozeman area on behalf of the local council. Here my climbing skills and expertise in the use of power tools were put to good use. [5]I was also involved in the development of new methods of tree preservation, which the council subsequently adopted as policy. The job also allowed me to demonstrate my leadership qualities and ability to work with a team.

I look forward to the opportunity of an interview.

Best regards,

Anthony Waite

WRITING

A Look at the picture to the left. What skills, personal qualities and certifications do you think are required to do this job?

B Read the job advertisement and answer the questions.

1. Which of the skills, qualities and certifications that you wrote down in Exercise A are mentioned?
2. Which are the most important for the job?

C **USING POWER VERBS** Read the cover letter. Rewrite the underlined sections using verbs to make the letter more powerful.

WRITING PRACTICE

A **PREPARE** Read the job advertisement and underline the key information regarding skills and certifications required.

Lifeguard – Team Leader at Ocean Resorts

We are looking for a dynamic individual to join our team at Ocean Resorts. Your role will be to support, coach and guide team members in creating a safe and fun environment.

The candidate will have proven experience in busy ocean and poolside environments and have a current American Red Cross Lifeguarding certification. Excellent physical fitness is essential, as well as being a strong swimmer.

A practical knowledge of first aid and a commitment to health and safety are also required. Flexibility in the role and the ability to take on extra responsibilities when required is a plus.

Applications to: Mr. Kevin Scholes, Manager, Ocean Resorts.

B **PLAN** You are going to write a cover letter in response to the ad for a lifeguard.

- Use the information you underlined in Exercise A.
- Organize your notes into an appropriate form for a cover letter.
- Use power verbs to talk about your achievements.

C **WRITE** Write your letter in 120–200 words.

VOCABULARY
Health problems

A Complete the text below with the words in the box.

dislocate fractured pressure pulled
rash rate sore sprained

B The words in bold are in the wrong sentence. Replace with the correct word.

1 Geoff's leg's in plaster because he **inflamed** ________________ it when he slipped on some ice.

2 I didn't warm up properly before the match and I **sore** ________________ a muscle.

3 My knee is very **fractured** ________________ – it has swelled up a lot so I'm putting ice on it.

4 A normal resting heart **blood** ________________ is 60 to 100 beats per minute.

5 If I fall asleep in a chair, I usually wake up with a **sprained** ________________ back.

6 Kate's **pulled** ________________ her ankle – she twisted it on the stairs but it's not too serious.

7 I have a **rate** ________________ on my skin and I don't know what's causing it.

8 The first thing the doctor did was to take my **rash** ________________ pressure.

HEALTH CHAT

Post your questions or medical issue on the HealthChat Portal and a qualified doctor will respond within minutes. You can post in both the private and public chat forums.

Woke up with a [1]________________ throat a few days ago, and a strange itchy red [2]________________ on my arms, chest and legs. Am seeing the doctor tomorrow …

Jared | 3:44 pm

Went for a ride last Saturday and noticed that my heart [3]________________ was much faster than usual. Got it checked out and found I have high blood [4]________________. My doctor thinks it might be stress-related.

Emily | 3:45 pm

Came off my mountain bike – again! – and [5]________________ my ankle. It was extremely painful, but could have been worse. The race medical team bandaged it up for me. Really glad it wasn't [6]________________ or broken!

Connor | 3:45 pm

Having [7]________________ a muscle in my leg about a month ago, I thought I was getting fit again – only to [8]________________ my shoulder this weekend. Really painful! And spent four hours in A&E!

Liz | 3:47 pm

GRAMMAR
Adjective clauses with complex relative pronouns

A Complete the sentences with one preposition in each blank.

1 The police were interested in interviewing victims ______ whose houses the burglars had broken.
2 The treadmill ______ which I was most interested is no longer for sale.
3 The brochure lists all the surfaces that the device can be attached ______.
4 He was very formal on the phone and said, '______ whom am I speaking?'
5 The thief stole a car, ______ which he made his getaway.
6 'I don't know who this package is for.' 'Well, who is it addressed ______?'
7 It's a wellness treatment ______ which I've read a lot recently.
8 There are six team members, ______ whom three are women.

B Rewrite the sentences using the word in parentheses.

1 This is the person. Her fitness business is now worth millions. (*whose*)
This is ______.
2 I trust Jonah. I trust him more than anyone. (*person*)
Jonah is ______.
3 I need a strategy which makes it impossible for me to get a virus. (*whereby*)
I need a strategy ______.
4 Be careful you don't get a training injury. You might never recover from it. (*from*)
Be careful you don't get ______.
5 We are targeting people. Exercise is not a priority for them. (*whom*)
We are targeting ______.
6 The owner of the company is very satisfied. The profits all go into his pockets. (*into*)
The owner of the company, ______.

PRONUNCIATION
Building suspense

A Read the sentences aloud. Use intonation and pauses to build suspense.

1 My health app told me that yesterday I did 5,000 steps!
2 Well, someone in this room has just passed their exams!
3 There's no more waiting – you get the results at the touch of a button.
4 I spent an hour shopping for spices and after all that, I didn't find the one I wanted.
5 It hasn't really sunk in yet but … I won first prize!
6 Do you want to hear the good news? Danny's getting out of the hospital … tomorrow!

8.1 **B Listen to the sentences from Exercise A.**

C Practice saying the sentences in the same way as the speakers do in Exercise B.

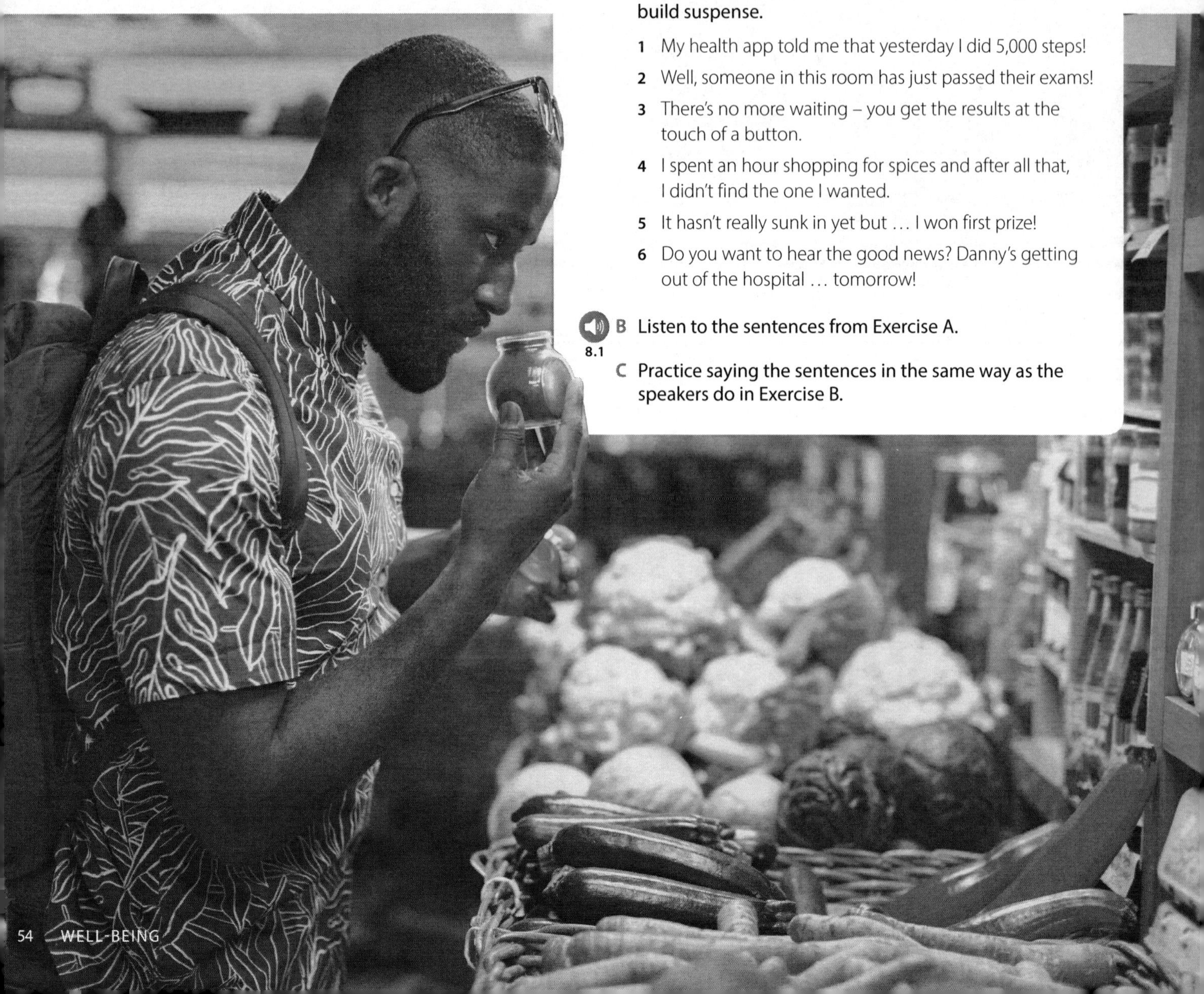

VOCABULARY

Idioms; Describing taste

A Choose the correct options to complete the text.

A TOUGH GAME

Only once had Roberto taken part in any kind of sporting competition, and that was in a tennis match. Someone persuaded him to play but his [1]***cup of tea / gut feeling*** was that he was making a terrible mistake!

A bigger mistake was watching his opponent play in a match before. That certainly [2]***made a meal of it / gave him food for thought*** because Roberto could see how good he was. Roberto very nearly [3]***got cold feet / kept an eye out***, but he decided to [4]***give it his best shot / take it with a pinch of salt***.

His opponent was very good and Roberto was clearly [5]***out of his depth / head and shoulders below him***. Roberto thought about [6]***moving the goalposts / throwing in the towel***, but he stuck at it. In the end, Roberto lost of course, but he likes to think he put up a good fight!

B Complete the sentences with one word to describe taste in each blank. The first letter is given to help you.

1. I don't like **f**____________ drinks like lemonade or soda.
2. **C**____________ vegetables like carrots, which you can really bite into, are a good substitute for chips.
3. I think the milk's gone **s**____________. Don't drink it.
4. Carol loves spicy food, but Mark prefers his to be **m**____________.
5. Jeanette always makes her food look really **a**____________.
6. Susan made a lovely smooth **c**____________ sauce to go with the mushrooms.
7. I like the **t**____________, slightly **a**____________ taste of grapefruit.
8. It's a terrible place. The meals they serve there are always **b**____________ and taste of nothing.
9. Their chips are usually covered in vinegar – far too **s**____________ for my taste.

PRONUNCIATION
Pronunciation of idioms

A Circle the words in the underlined idioms which are stressed. Then practice saying the sentences.

1. No, tennis isn't really my cup of tea.
2. I know it was a penalty, but he really made a meal of it, rolling all over the field like that!
3. Murphy didn't take part in the robbery – he was only there to keep an eye out for the police.
4. He exaggerates a lot, so you can take most of what he says with a grain of salt.
5. Eva was the best student in our class – she was head and shoulders above the rest of us.
6. We knew where we were at the beginning of this project, but if the boss keeps moving the goalposts, we'll never get anywhere.

8.2 **B Listen to the sentences from Exercise A.**

C Practice saying the sentences in the same way as the speakers do in Exercise B.

GRAMMAR
Pronouns and determiners

A Choose the correct options to complete the sentences.

1. It would be better for all of us if we did *any* / *more* exercise.
2. There was a choice of two desserts, but I didn't want *either* / *neither*.
3. *Most people* / *The most people* feel better when they are active.
4. Do you want some coffee? I'll make you *some* / *some coffee.*
5. Some people like team sports, but *others people* / *others* prefer individual activities.
6. There were *a few* / *very few* members there, so they postponed the meeting until the following week.
7. One *of* / *from* the fitness programs is bound to interest you.
8. There's *a little* / *little* point in worrying about it – we can't change anything now.

B Find and correct the mistakes in the sentences.

1. When you're doing a serious hike, you can't drink too much of water – in fact, most people don't drink enough.
   ______
2. There were two vegan options, but I didn't like or want both of them.
   ______
3. They who followed the diet reported an average loss of three kilos in the first week.
   ______
4. You have too much sugar and salt in your diet – it's best if you cut back on neither.
   ______
5. There are only few restaurants that serve good vegetarian food in this city.
   ______
6. You drink a lot of coffee, and I think you'd sleep better if you drank less of.
   ______
7. These are your books – my are still over there where I left them.
   ______
8. Jamie only needs six hours of sleep a night, but I can never seem to get enough of.
   ______

a

b

FOOD, GLORIOUS FOOD

We are what we eat? Well I'm not sure what this received wisdom means if you're on a charcoal diet! With so much advice about food and eating available to us today, it can be hard to know what is good information and what can be downright harmful. With a growing global wellness industry eager to package and push us a never-ending stream of diets and food products, we decided to take a closer look at some of the diets out there currently.

Charcoal

Black cheese or black ice cream, anyone? Almost any foodstuff can be made black by adding activated charcoal. The thinking behind this is that charcoal is a porous form of carbon which supposedly absorbs harmful bacteria in the digestive system. While this may be true, critics of the diet argue that activated charcoal is so greedy it absorbs anything in your stomach, even the good stuff like food, vitamins and the medicines you might be taking. Not surprisingly, the fans of this diet don't accept this. I don't know about you, but, for me, variety of color is a major 'ingredient' in the enjoyment of food. So that's one thing that would make it harder for me to follow this diet.

Ketogenic

Sounds rather scientific, doesn't it? The keto diet, as it is called, allegedly turns your body into a fat-burning machine by avoiding carbohydrates such as pasta. Admittedly, those who have tried it swear that it works and have lost weight and benefited from improved health associated with weight loss. Like most diets, though, this one also has its critics, who argue that any diet that excludes an entire food group from its regimen is bound to have some side-effects, or not provide all the nutrition we need. But if losing weight is your goal, you could give it a try.

Cauliflower

Not just cauliflower, but cabbage, or any diet that claims sticking to any one foodstuff will bring rapid and amazing results. Cauliflower, it seems, can replace bread as a principal foodstuff! You can even get cauliflower pizza crust! There's no doubt that cauliflower is good for you; it is rich in anti-oxidants, is anti-inflammatory, is full of vitamin C and other vitamins and helps with digestion. It is also thought to improve both heart and brain health. But some dieticians and nutritionists advise that it should just be a part, along with other vegetables, of a well-balanced diet.

Vegan

Veganism seems to be very popular right now. Strict vegans will have nothing to do with any foodstuff that comes from animals. As well as meat and fish, they reject basic everyday foods such as milk, butter, eggs, even honey. Interestingly some vegans claim to enjoy better physical and mental health as a result – but critics might respond: well, they would, wouldn't they? Not all vegans do it for health reasons. They adopt veganism as a way of life, believing that modern farming methods are cruel to animals and harmful to the environment. It is an ethical diet, but opinions vary as to how filling or satisfying vegan meals are – gastronomically, that is.

READING

A SKIM Read *Food, glorious food* quickly. Match the diet plans to the pictures (a–d).

B READ FOR DETAIL Read the article again and answer the questions.

1 Which diet is said to be good for weight loss?
2 Which diet is said to be a larger lifestyle choice?
3 Which diet might have a negative effect on digestion?

C READ TO IDENTIFY OPINIONS Read the article again. Underline examples of the following.

1 Adverbs to show a positive attitude
2 Adverbs to show a negative attitude
3 Attitude to reported information
4 Use of colloquial asides, tag questions and rhetorical questions to comment on information

Glossary

gastronomist (n) person who studies the art of eating well
porous (adj) having a lot of very small holes so that air or water can pass through

D REFLECT Are any of the diets popular in your country?

c

d

LISTENING

A PREDICT You are going to listen to a radio interview about astronauts and well-being. What do you think might be some of the challenges of this kind of work?

8.3 **B LISTEN FOR GIST** Listen to the interview. Some parts are somewhat hard to hear because of interference on the line. Were any of your ideas from Exercise A mentioned?

8.3 **C LISTEN WITH NOISE** Listen to the interview again and choose the correct options (a or b).

1 Angela Schneider specializes in
  - **a** research into weight loss and healthy eating.
  - **b** nutrition and diet for astronauts.

2 What does Angela say about iron in the blood of a space traveler?
  - **a** There's too much.
  - **b** There's too little.

3 Astronauts are more likely
  - **a** to break their bones when they come back.
  - **b** to follow a strength training program.

4 According to Angela, the food which astronauts eat today is
  - **a** delicious.
  - **b** unappetizing.

8.3 **D LISTEN FOR DETAIL** Listen again. Write notes on what you hear in the table below.

1 Key elements of an astronaut's diet	
2 Injuries that an astronaut could suffer after returning to Earth	
3 Measures to prevent injuries	
4 Amount of iron in an astronaut's blood	
5 Food items which appear on the menu	

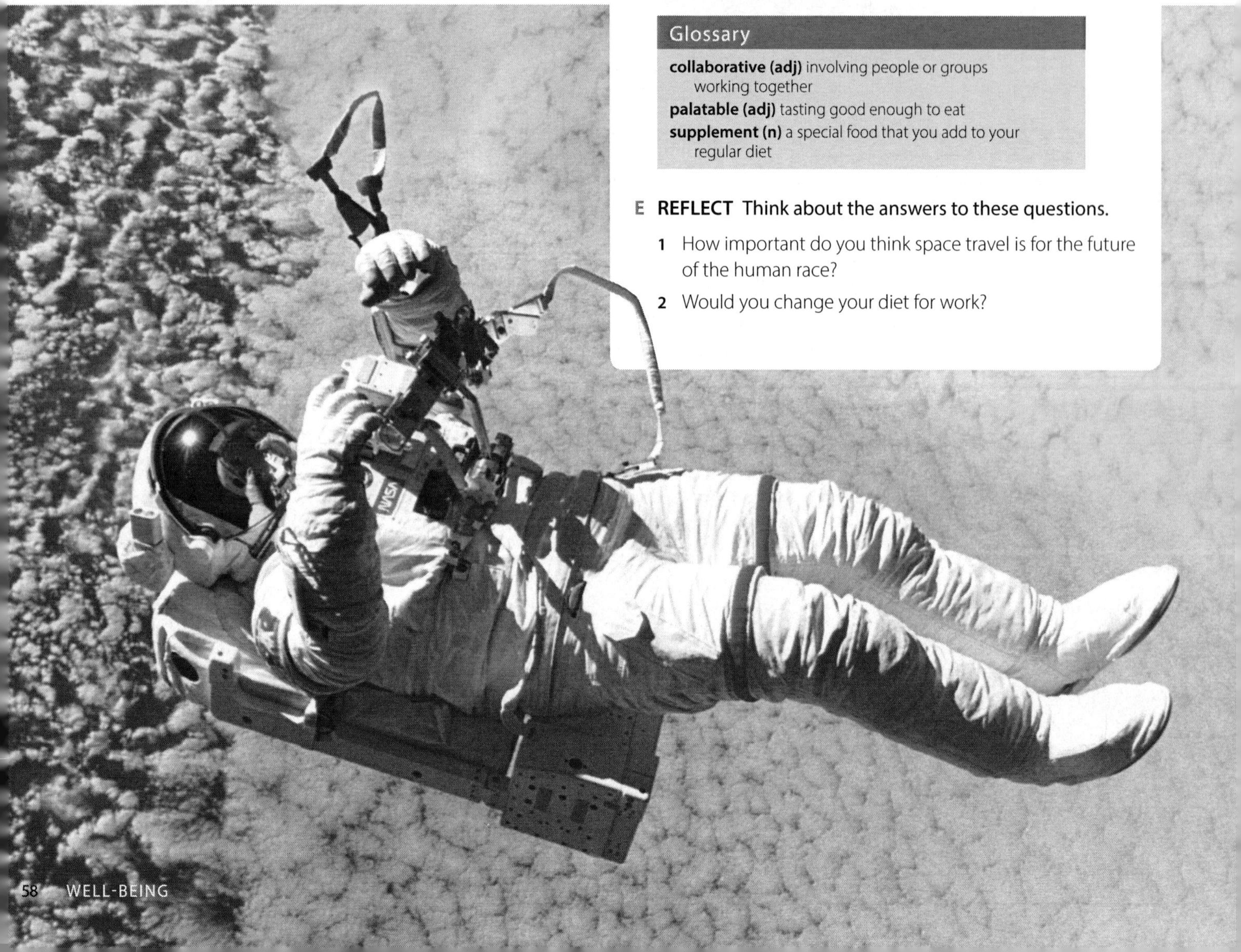

Glossary

collaborative (adj) involving people or groups working together
palatable (adj) tasting good enough to eat
supplement (n) a special food that you add to your regular diet

E REFLECT Think about the answers to these questions.

1 How important do you think space travel is for the future of the human race?

2 Would you change your diet for work?

8.5 Well-being

Write a summary

WRITING

A What physical and psychological effects might 'overtraining' have on an athlete?

B Read the first paragraph of *Time to slow down?* and complete the tasks.

1. Underline the keywords.
2. Which is the best one-sentence summary of the paragraph (a, b or c)? Give reasons for your choice.
   - **a** Consult a doctor before undertaking a training program and devise your own programs to avoid overtraining.
   - **b** Overtraining syndrome is the result of training too much and typically leads to both physical and psychological symptoms.
   - **c** Too much training can push the body beyond its capacity to recover and both physiological and psychological symptoms may present themselves.

C **PARAPHRASING** Now read the second paragraph of the article and complete the tasks.

1. Underline the keywords and ideas.
2. What is the main focus of this paragraph?
3. Write a one- or two-sentence summary of this paragraph.

D Read the rest of the article and note down keywords and ideas.

WRITING PRACTICE

A **PREPARE** Read *Time to slow down?* again. Think about the answers to these questions and write notes.

1. What are the main points of each paragraph?
2. Which words (proper nouns, technical vocabulary) can you reuse in your summary?
3. Which parts of the text are unnecessary for your summary?

B **PLAN** You are going to write a summary of *Time to slow down?*

- Organize your notes from Writing Exercises B–D.
- Use your own words as much as possible. Check that you have not repeated unnecessary phrases or structures from the article.
- Make sure you have included all the key points.

C **WRITE** Write your summary in approximately 60 words.

TIME TO SLOW DOWN?

Consistency in strength, mobility and cardiovascular training is often held up as a key determiner for success and receiving the full health benefits of these types of exercise. But sometimes there is a fine line between consistency and what is known as 'overtraining syndrome'. Put simply, too much training can force the body beyond its capacity to recover. Those that push themselves hard in sports professionally or recreationally may be especially at risk. According to research by the *Journal of Athletic Training*, both physiological and psychological symptoms may present themselves when overtraining occurs.

Physiological symptoms

Various physical symptoms of overtraining include unexplained muscle and weight loss, an inability to build muscle among male athletes and excessive thirst. The cardiovascular system can be affected, with increased heart rate and a greater length of time to return to a normal heart rate, and both increased and decreased levels of blood pressure. Another common indicator is injury, which may occur as a result of the kind of loads used in training or because the body is unable to recover from training. Furthermore, there may be an increased risk of infections such as colds.

Psychological symptoms

It is not necessarily as easy to determine overtraining from psychological symptoms but if, for example, athletes find themselves generally run-down or mentally unprepared for training, this may be a warning sign. Sleep disturbance, tiredness and loss of energy all suggest potential overtraining. Emotional mood may also provide a clue, as mood swings and feelings of irritability and anger have been commonly observed. The self-confidence of an athlete may also decrease while levels of cortisol (stress hormones) might rise. Finally, it's sensible to keep an eye on the regularity of meals as loss of appetite has been noted as a symptom.

Prevention and treatment

The advice of medical professionals should be sought in cases of overtraining. Trainers and coaches also have a particularly important role to play in monitoring athletes for symptoms, as well as devising training programs that prevent injury. Beyond recognizing symptoms, action must be taken to tackle them, for example, through periods of rest or decreases in training intensity. It is possible to address psychological symptoms as well, by modifying programs and sometimes allowing athletes more autonomy in the design of a program.

VOCABULARY
Slang

A Choose the correct options to complete the sentences.

1 Mark was ***awesome / stoked / bummed*** when he got a place at the college he wanted to go to.

2 Jack's always ***whining / hanging out / chilling out*** about not having any money, but he doesn't go out and look for a job!

3 In the UK, people refer informally to a male stranger as a ***buddy / guy / bloke***, but in the US, he might be called a ***buck / dude / grand***.

4 $100 for a laptop? That sounds like a ***shady / crash / beat*** deal to me – are you sure it's not ***excellent / taken care of / stolen***?

5 They offered to buy me a ***TV / shambles / grand***, but I was ***cos / do / like***, what do I want that for? I need some ***crash / wheels / bucks*** so I can get around!

B Read the extract from a story. Replace the words and phrases in italics with slang expressions from the box.

broke bucks could do with crashed grand in good shape set her back shambles

1 ______ 5 ______
2 ______ 6 ______
3 ______ 7 ______
4 ______ 8 ______

Rose Robinson woke up and took a look around her apartment. It was a [1]*mess*. She'd come home at who knows what time and [2]*fallen asleep* on the couch.

She knew she [3]*would benefit from* finding a new place, but she also knew that it would [4]*cost* at least a [5]*thousand dollars* and she just didn't have that kind of money.

She looked in her pocket, 'Seven [6]*dollars*! I'm sick and tired of being [7]*without money*,' she muttered to herself, 'I need some money fast and then I'll be [8]*fine*!' Just then, a dangerous and life-changing plan started to form in her sleepy brain.

PRONUNCIATION
Pronouncing vague expressions

A Underline the vague expressions in the sentences. How would you pronounce them?

1 I feel kind of strange – like I've been here before or something.

2 We have to give a talk, or a speech, or something like that.

3 I have to do some jobs – shopping, cleaning and so on.

4 You know, I think that, in some way or another, he must be involved.

5 So, in a sense, this is the easiest job in the world!

6 What do you take me for – some sort of fool?

7 Don't give me excuses like you overslept or whatever.

8 My course covers health and safety issues, stuff like that.

9.1 **B** Listen to the sentences from Exercise A.

C Practice saying the sentences in the same way as the speakers do in Exercise B.

GRAMMAR
Noun phrases

A Underline two noun phrases in each sentence.

1 Those students who haven't completed the assignment should stay behind at the end of the lecture.

2 Both of the solutions he suggested sounded a little like a desperate attempt to please the boss.

3 He invested all the money he'd saved up into some crazy get-rich-quick scheme and lost everything.

4 The thing that annoys Pierre most is the way young people don't seem to care about language.

5 Three of the 20 people present were first-time attendees.

6 The idea that simply punishing children teaches them to behave has fallen out of favor with many modern educationalists.

7 Do you know a good place to eat that would suit a group of hungry teenagers?

8 Sometimes it seems to me that almost everyone I know is hooked on some computer game or other.

B Find and correct the mistakes in the sentences.

1 I spend all my free time almost doing sports.

____

2 The belief what you can change things is all you need in order to make a difference.

____

3 The person where I spoke to didn't seem to have a clue what was happening.

____

4 I need a place for staying for a few days.

____

5 Both of ideas seem a little hard to put into practice.

____

6 The woman who sitting next to Claire is Frances.

____

7 Very few of people in this country have traveled abroad.

____

8 The interviewer was impressed by the fact how I knew so much about their company.

____

C Complete each sentence with one word only.

1 Unfortunately ____________ of the students failed yesterday's history exam – only a few passed.

2 ____________ man sitting at the bus stop works in a science laboratory.

3 Out of all my colleagues, Daniel is the ____________ I trust the most.

4 Few members ____________ the community spoke out against the mayor.

5 Unlike ours, ____________ study was well funded, so they could afford the best equipment.

6 The fact ____________ I love communication affected my decision to study languages.

PRONUNCIATION
Intrusive stops

A Read the sentences aloud, paying attention to the way you pronounce the underlined sections.

1. A lot of youngsters enjoy going out to dance.
2. Hamsters build nests for warmth.
3. It must be nice being a prince, but your life would be pretty intense.
4. I did four lengths of the pool, but I didn't have the strength to do more.
5. Once you get into trouble for something, it can influence the way other people see you.

9.2 **B** Listen to the sentences from Exercise A.

C Practice saying the sentences in the same way as the speakers do in Exercise B.

VOCABULARY
Verb + object + base form; Gestures and body language

A Match the beginnings of the sentences (1–8) to the endings (a–h).

1. Listen! I think I can hear someone ....
2. A thoughtful family friend let me ....
3. The manager had us ....
4. I heard a dog ....
5. Not only must justice be done, but it must also be seen ....
6. I wonder if you could help me ....
7. I thought I could feel something ....
8. Were you made ....

a climbing up my leg.
b bark once, and then there was silence.
c coming. Don't make a sound.
d fill in this form. It looks difficult.
e to sign any documents when you started working there?
f drive her car to see if it suited me.
g to be done.
h wait for an hour before she spoke to us.

B Choose the correct options to complete the story.

When John caught up with Sharon, she was sitting on a rock, [1]***gazing / crossing / bending*** out to sea. She held something in her hand that she was [2]***folding / fidgeting / shaking*** with.

'Are you OK?' John said gently. She just [3]***shrugged / smirked / grinned*** her shoulders.

Then she [4]***glared / nodded / shook*** her head and said, 'No, I'm not OK!'

'Sharon, what's wrong?' John asked. She turned to look at him and [5]***winked / blinked / wiggled*** her eyes a few times as the bright sun lit up her face.

She took the ring off her finger, stood up and [6]***beckoned / stared / leaned*** him to follow her to the water's edge. She [7]***bent / pointed / folded*** back across the beach and said 'That was where we met'. She threw the ring into the ocean.

John [8]***grinned / crossed / raised*** his eyebrows and stood open-mouthed, too shocked to react.

GRAMMAR

Participle clauses and verbless clauses

A Complete the second sentence so that it has a similar meaning to the first sentence. Write between two and five words, including the word given.

1 Because she got out of bed early, Nina had the view of the city all to herself.
UP
____________, Nina had the view of the city all to herself.

2 I didn't know anything about math, but I still worked out the answer.
DESPITE
____________ anything about math, I still worked out the answer.

3 If you do the job properly, it shouldn't take more than a day.
DONE
____________ shouldn't take more than a day.

4 As I am not practical, it made more sense after I had read the instructions.
READING
____________ instructions meant it made more sense.

5 He was not interested in any special offers because he had bought a new phone yesterday.
JUST
____________ phone yesterday, he was not interested in any special offers.

6 If you give them a positive environment, most children will learn quickly and easily.
RIGHT
____________ environment, most children will learn quickly and easily.

B Find and correct the mistakes with participle and verbless clauses.

1 They were feeling threatened, the animals instinctively hid behind the wall.

____

2 Had never been on a plane before, I was both excited and nervous.

____

3 If you successful in your application, you will be notified by email.

____

4 Grown up in the US, Marvin has always spoken English well.

____

5 Been exhausted and short on money, Carrie cut short her trip to Bolivia.

____

6 Before started work in insurance, Lionel was a factory worker.

____

7 Despite I hadn't been there before, I soon found my way around.

____

8 While suffering badly from the flu, a couple of close friends visited Angela every day.

____

C Choose the correct options (a, b or c) to complete the text.

Languages contain so much of a people's culture that it's a shame that more isn't done to preserve them. [1] ____________, I find languages infinitely fascinating. I thought I might be able to help preserve African languages, [2] ____________ much of my youth there.

Many of these languages, [3] ____________ by just a handful of people, are dying. [4] ____________ in funds to preserve them themselves, many tribes are destined to lose a valuable part of their heritage. So I applied to work with an association whose mission is to preserve the culture of several African tribes.

[5] ____________ the head of the association, I felt inspired to get to work. However, we must frequently rely on the elders of a community, who, [6] ____________ how to read or write, struggle with transcribing words and phrases. This presents further challenges with accurate translation.

	a	b	c
1	A linguist	Being a linguist	To be a linguist
2	while to spend	spent	having spent
3	having spoken	speaking	spoken
4	Lacked	Lacking	Being lacking
5	After meeting	Being met	Despite meeting
6	never teaching	having never been taught	having never taught

WORDS *have* POWER

In a well-documented experiment (Bargh, Chen and Burrows, 1996), students at New York University were given five words which they had to use in order to construct sentences of four words (i.e. they had to leave one word out). They did this 30 times. Of the 30 groups of words, 15 contained words related in some way either to rudeness (e.g. *disturb* or *annoyingly*) or politeness (e.g. *respect* or *patiently*). There was also a neutral set, containing words that were neither connected to rudeness nor politeness (e.g. *give* or *occasionally*). Students didn't know whether they had the 'rude set', the 'polite set' or the 'neutral set'. In fact, they thought the experiment was simply to test their speed in forming grammatically correct sentences.

Participants were told to come and find the experimenter when they were finished. What they didn't realize was that this was really the important part of the experiment, because the researchers had staged a delay, whereby the student was forced to wait while the experimenter was deeply involved in a conversation with another 'participant' (in reality, another researcher). Unknown to the student, a stopwatch had been activated the moment they stood up from the task with the sentences. The purpose of the experiment was to see how long the students would wait before interrupting.

READING

A PREDICT Do you think that words or names have the power to change people's behavior? How?

B READ FOR GIST Read *Words have power* quickly. Were any of your ideas in Exercise A mentioned? Have you changed your opinion? Why/Why not?

C READ FOR DETAIL Read the article again. Are these sentences true (T) or false (F)? Correct the sentences that are false.

1. Students were asked to make 30 sentences of 4 words each. *T / F*
2. The experiment was to see how fast they could form sentences. *T / F*
3. Participants were timed to see how quickly they completed the task. *T / F*
4. Most of the participants waited ten minutes after the task. *T / F*
5. The last paragraph suggests that we purposely avoid basing major life choices on how similar things are to our own name. *T / F*

D READ FOR OUTCOMES Read the article again and take notes on ways to answer the questions.

1. What was the purpose of the experiment?
2. What were the main results?
3. What conclusions were drawn?
4. What do you think about the results of the experiment?

Glossary

neutral (adj) neither one thing nor its opposite
stage (v) make someone believe that something is real

E REFLECT Think about the answers to these questions.

1. Do you think that names could influence people to choose different careers? Why/Why not?
2. Can you think of any other ways that words can influence social behavior?

As expected, students who had been exposed to the 'rude' words interrupted the soonest, followed by the neutral group and, lastly, the students who had just processed 'polite' words.

John Bargh, who devised the experiment, admitted that we should not rush to the conclusion that exposure to rude or polite words makes us behave in that way. In fact, one of the problems with such a conclusion is that, in the experiment described above, 21 of the 34 participants did not interrupt at all in the 10 minutes that they were kept waiting. However, Bargh re-analyzed the results and looked only at those who had interrupted. Of these, over 60 percent had just processed the 'rude' words.

Is there more evidence to suggest that words play a more important role than we once thought? Pelham, Mirdenberg and Jones (2012) have suggested that our name – as one of the words that we learn first and hold dear – influences whether we like other people and things with similar names. In the most surprising results, it was shown that more people named Dennis had chosen dentistry as a profession. Similarly, more women named Laura, and more men named Lawrence, became lawyers. Similar links have been shown between a person's name and the place they choose to live, as well as their choice of a husband or wife.

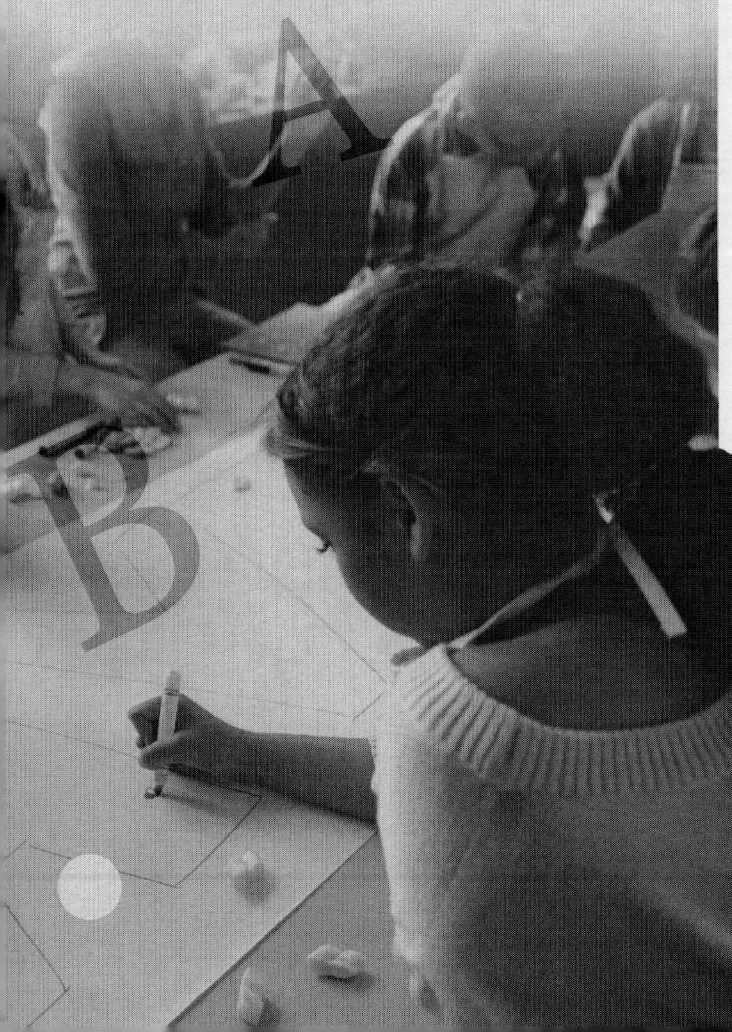

LISTENING

A PREDICT Check (✓) the skills you think are important at school.

- passing exams ☐
- practical skills ☐
- developing your imagination ☐
- thinking independently ☐
- developing personal interests ☐
- artistic skills ☐
- physical exercise ☐

9.3 **B LISTEN FOR GIST** Listen to a conversation about education. Were any of your skills in Exercise A mentioned?

9.3 **C LISTEN FOR DETAIL** Listen again. Are these sentences true (T) or false (F)?

1 Cassie is new to the area. *T / F*
2 The Steiner education method places great emphasis on creativity. *T / F*
3 Rob and Cassie agree that passing exams is not a legitimate educational goal. *T / F*
4 Inspections at Rob and Sandy's school create tension. *T / F*
5 Steiner school courses are designed to meet the needs of individual students. *T / F*
6 The curriculum at the Steiner school is broadly similar to a mainstream school. *T / F*

9.4 **D LISTEN TO RAPID SPEECH** Listen to some extracts from the discussion. Cross out words and sounds that the speakers leave out. Put brackets [ ] around the phrases they link together. The first two have been done for you.

1 [Nice ~~to~~ meet ~~you~~.] How ~~are~~ ~~you~~ doing?
2 So … ~~have~~ you just moved here, Cassie?
3 I've lived here for … let me see … for four years.
4 Because it's you know … it's really *unique* and stuff.
5 Is it one of those places where you can, you know, do anything you want?

E REFLECT Think about the answers to these questions.

1 Which is the most important skill developed at school? Why?
2 How could secondary schools in your country be improved? Think of examples.

WRITING

A PREDICT Look at the pictures. What do you think it feels like to be in one of these crowds? Do people behave differently when they are in a crowd? Why?

B Read the conclusion to an academic report and match the topics (a–d) to the paragraphs (1–4).

- **a** Areas that still need investigation ____
- **b** Summary of theories researched ____
- **c** Aims of research ____
- **d** What was learned ____

C LINKING IN ACADEMIC WRITING Read the conclusion again and complete it with the linking words and phrases (a–e). Sometimes more than one option is possible.

- **a** However
- **b** On the other hand
- **c** Additionally
- **d** Nonetheless
- **e** Admittedly

D Underline two sentences where a colon is used to show that one idea explains another. Underline two sentences where a semi-colon is used to show that two related ideas are of equal importance.

WRITING PRACTICE

A PREPARE Choose a piece of academic research or use your imagination and take notes on the points you will make in your conclusion.

B PLAN You are going to write a conclusion to an academic report.

- Organize your notes from Exercise A into an appropriate structure for the conclusion to an academic report.
- Use linking words, colons and semi-colons to show the relationship between ideas.

C WRITE Write your conclusion in 200–300 words.

Conclusion

1 Our research set out to examine theories of crowd behavior, beginning with classic contagion and convergence theories, which have been the basis of all subsequent theories. It became clear that most of the research so far stems from disciplines such as psychology and sociology; there has been little recent research into crowd behavior at large outdoor events.

2 Contagion theory states that individuals are protected by their membership of the crowd and that individual responsibility is ignored: normal values and the ability to reason are abandoned. [1] ___, ideas and emotions within the crowd become contagious and spread rapidly. [2] ___, convergence theorists argue that individuals in a crowd do not lose personal identity: personal beliefs and values are communicated and crowd behavior depends on shared feelings and beliefs. [3] ___, some individuals may well exploit the anonymity of being in a crowd to take part in antisocial behaviors they normally would not.

3 It seems clear, then, that once individuals join a group they become part of a group personality. [4] ___, our research revealed that there are many factors that can influence the behavior of individuals in a crowd: crowd catalysts such as police presence, the space available, type of event and so on. We will be conducting further research in this area.

4 While both theories form the basis of most research into crowd behavior, they assume some kind of antisocial behavior is the outcome. They fail to demonstrate why some crowds remain passive and why individuals in a crowd who hold similar beliefs behave differently; nor do they examine the difference between organized and spontaneous crowds. [5] ___, we believe that these theories are still useful in understanding mass behavior in general.

VOCABULARY

Culture and heritage; Nouns with *to*

A Complete the sentences with the words in the box.

architectural designated endangered funds habitats heritage preserve refurbish ruins settlement

1 Some areas near the city have been __________ national parks so they can't be built on.
2 Because their __________ are threatened, many species are __________.
3 The unique __________ qualities of these buildings make them an important part of our country's __________.
4 The __________ found by archaeologists are said to be part of a __________ going back thousands of years.
5 We would like to at least __________ these houses to stop the damage getting worse until there are enough __________ available to __________ them.

B Complete the article with one word in each blank. The first and last letters and the number of letters needed are given to help you.

Building a future

For anyone who has the [1]**u**__________**e** (*4*) to go into city planning, we need you – but don't expect an easy ride. What you need more than anything is the [2]**d**__________**e** (*6*) to create better living conditions for city dwellers. It will be your [3]**r**__________**y** (*14*) to make sure that the future does not become a nightmare scenario. You will have an [4]**o**__________**n** (*10*) to future generations and you should be ready to improve things.

Why is it so hard? Well, historically, we have seen a [5]**f**__________**e** (*7*) to learn from the mistakes of the past. We have also seen a flat [6]**r**__________**l** (*7*) to adopt green measures and sometimes a general reluctance to think more than a few years into the future. There is a problem in that people often have a [7]**t**__________**y** (*8*) to only do things that will benefit them in the short term. Sometimes, these people need a [8]**r**__________**r** (*8*) to focus on long-term solutions as well.

PRONUNCIATION
Introducing new information

A Read the sentences aloud. Does the pitch go up or down on the underlined words?

1 I enjoyed getting to see some of the sights. <u>And</u> I made some great friends on my travels.
2 There's no doubt that travel broadens the mind. <u>On the other hand</u>, you won't learn much about a culture if you stay in a resort and never go exploring.
3 Some older vacationers tend to be happy with relaxed beach vacations and a bit of light sightseeing, <u>whereas</u> younger tourists usually want a little bit more action.
4 You're going to Cyprus? I love Cyprus. <u>As a matter of fact</u>, I was born there!
5 I know a lot of people find traveling exciting, <u>but for me</u> it's always really stressful.
6 I know tourism brings money to companies, <u>but at the same time</u>, I wonder how much ordinary people benefit from it.
7 I love traveling overseas. <u>And</u> it's good for the economy of the countries you visit.
8 Tourism isn't always beneficial to countries in many ways. <u>And in fact</u>, some resorts are now looking for ways to discourage big numbers of people.

10.1 **B Listen to the sentences to check your answers to Exercise A.**

GRAMMAR
Discourse markers

A Match numbers (1–10) to letters (a–j) to form full sentences.

1 There are so many European countries, for instance, ___
2 I don't like traveling very much. As a matter of fact, ___
3 We spent most of our trip in Bolivia. Conversely, ___
4 They cut their vacation short owing to the fact ___
5 I'm happy to fly everywhere, whereas ___
6 He claims he doesn't travel, yet ___
7 Some cities suffer from a big problem, namely, ___
8 I think it's the best museum in the world, ___
9 We enjoyed the sights despite ___
10 My summer in Spain was very relaxing. Moreover, ___

a he went on three vacations last year!
b that they were running out of money.
c I hate it!
d it really helped me get to grips with the language.
e the fact that there were huge crowds.
f the best I've been to in any case.
g that there are too many tourists.
h Belgium, that I still haven't visited.
i we only had two days in Venezuela.
j my husband says it's better to travel slowly by boat or train.

B Complete the second sentence so that it has a similar meaning to the first sentence. Write between two and five words, including the word given.

1 Although it was a long journey there, we enjoyed the view of the mountain immensely.
DESPITE
We enjoyed ourselves immensely ____________________
a long journey.

2 We didn't go to Warsaw, but it didn't matter because I've been there before.
CASE
We didn't go to Warsaw, but in ____________________
been there before.

3 There are two countries I really want to visit, and they are Australia and China.
NAMELY
There are two countries I really want to visit, ____________________.

4 The bad weather prevented us from going to the national park.
OWING
We didn't go to the national park ____________________.

5 The return journey seemed very quick compared to the outward journey.
WHEREAS
The outward journey seemed to take a long time, ____________________
very quick.

6 To tell you the truth, I wouldn't mind if I never got on another plane in my life.
MATTER
____________________, I wouldn't mind if I never got on another plane in my life.

10.2 Society

How to change the world

VOCABULARY
Word building

A Choose the correct options (a, b or c) to complete the sentences.

1 She loves her job – she's very ___ about it.
   a passion
   b passionate
   c passionhood

2 Nobody knew the ___ of the mystery donor.
   a identity
   b identify
   c identification

3 I grew up in a really run-down ___.
   a neighborly
   b neighbor
   c neighborhood

4 Clark wanted to enter ___ life as soon as possible after graduating.
   a politics
   b politician
   c political

5 Some countries make you take a ___ test in order to adopt their nationality.
   a citizenship
   b citizen
   c citizenry

6 It was totally ___ of you to mention her brother – you know they don't speak to each other.
   a insensible
   b senseless
   c insensitive

7 Depositing huge sums of money in offshore accounts may be legal, but is it ___?
   a ethics
   b ethical
   c ethic

8 Charles is responsible for internet ___ at his company.
   a secure
   b securely
   c security

B Complete the text with words from the box with a correct suffix. Make any other necessary spelling changes.

apathy	commune	effect	passion	person	persuade

To change the world quickly, you have to be [1] ___________ about your beliefs, you need to have a(n) [2] ___________ strategy and you need good [3] ___________ skills – such as being extremely friendly, polite and, of course, [4] ___________ – so that people will listen to you.

Sometimes, however, the best changes are the ones that take place little by little. If you can find a way to stop people from being [5] ___________ and to make them care about their [6] ___________, the results will slowly but surely become global.

GRAMMAR
Ellipsis and substitution

A Cross out any words that can be omitted.

1 Some people think we can change the world but I don't think we can change the world.

2 If you get the opportunity to go, you should take the opportunity to go.

3 A lot of people struggle with course fees and I wish they didn't struggle with course fees.

4 They should target governments and they should target large companies.

5 We're going to have food and we're going to have music.

6 You asked me if I thought we could make a difference and the answer is yes I do think we can make a difference.

7 I know a lot of people who are pessimistic about the future, but I'm not pessimistic about the future.

8 Are you joining us for pizza? Do you have any preference as to what we order?

B Complete the sentences with a phrase including *do, does, so* or *not*. Write one or two words in each blank.

1 I take a short vacation away from everything. I ______________ to clear my head when I'm stressed at work.

2 He said he can't come, but I'm hoping he'll change his mind. Let me know if ______________.

3 I might go to the stores later, so I'll let you know if ______________.

4 Johnny went white-water rafting. I could never ______________.

5 'Will you be finished before four?'' I expect ______________.'

6 You might need to access the archives. In order to ______________, ask one of the technical support team.

7 'We might have to do this again.' 'I ______________ – it took us days.'

8 'I'm planning to spend all my money on a sports car!' 'Why on Earth would you ______________?'

PRONUNCIATION
Managing conversations

A Read the sentences aloud. Try to say the underlined words according to the instructions in parentheses. Pay attention to whether your intonation rises or falls.

1

A: So, then I plan to travel to Cambodia.

B: <u>Right</u>. (because you think the speaker has finished/you want to say something yourself)

2

A: The chairperson said there might be an opening for me.

B: <u>OK</u>. (showing excitement/enthusiasm)

3

A: There'd be a team of four initially, then six, then eight or more.

B: <u>OK</u>. (hesitant, needing clarification)

4

A: I think it's a great opportunity.

B: <u>Right</u>. (sarcastic, unenthusiastic)

5

A: I'm planning to apply for a job there.

B: <u>I see</u>! (genuinely interested)

10.2 **B Listen to the conversations from Exercise A. Do the speakers say the underlined words in the same way as you did?**

READING

A READ FOR GIST Read three short newspaper articles. Which urban problem(s) do they discuss?

B SYNTHESIZE INFORMATION Read the articles again. Complete the table using information from all three articles.

	Problems	Solutions	Criticism of solutions
UK			
Paris			
Freiburg			

Parking just got PRICIER

In another move to fight congestion and pollution in the UK's most gridlocked cities, councils may impose a workplace parking fee of up to $1000, to be paid for by employers rather than employees. Growing concerns about the effects of congestion and air pollution on residents' health, including asthma and bronchitis, have led to the move.

Some opponents of the plan say they have seen no evidence that fewer people were driving to work and that it could lead to job losses. Also it would force more people into using an already overcrowded public transportation system.

A spokesman for the Automobile Association (AA) said that instead of taxing businesses, who may be forced to leave the area or stop trading, we should be concentrating on getting people to switch to electric vehicles.

By law, all funds gained from such charges are to be invested in improving public transportation and infrastructure.

Paris' TRAFFIC PROBLEMS

The authorities in Paris have tried almost everything to reduce congestion and the mayor wants to reduce the number of cars entering the city by making life difficult for drivers.

With concerns raised about premature death due to air pollution, Paris has now made permanent a sticker system. All vehicles in Paris must display an anti-pollution sticker or face a fine of $68 for cars and $138 for trucks. The stickers cost $4.18. Yet a recent police check found that only 1 in 50 vehicles stopped had the sticker.

About 600,000 vehicles drive around the city each day and most come in from the suburbs. Concerns have been raised by those traveling from the suburbs who are not as well connected by the public transportation system. One driver complained, 'We're being taxed off the roads. It's not our fault. They should get the car manufacturers to make cars that don't pollute.'

As green as it gets?

It is obviously easier to deal with urban problems in a small city with a population of fewer than half a million people, but maybe larger cities with traffic problems could take a page or two from Freiburg's book. For a start, the entire city center was pedestrianized back in 1973, and city authorities have developed an integrated system of 500 kilometers of bike routes, cable cars and a public transportation system that is efficient, comfortable and above all cheap. In fact, those who choose to live without a car at all are offered cheap housing and free public transportation.

Preference is given to environmentally friendly modes of transportation such as walking, biking and public transportation, and smart urban planning has made it a city of short distances where people's needs can be met within walking distance. All this has made Freiburg one of the greenest and most pollution-free cities in Europe.

Glossary

disincentive (n) a plan/action that makes you not want to do something

gridlocked (adj) with so much traffic congestion that vehicles cannot move at all

take a page out of/from somebody's book (idiom) to copy somebody else's actions because they are successful

C REFLECT Is it worth owning a car in a big city?

LISTENING

A **PREDICT** Read the ad. Would you be interested in applying for this job? What skills would you need? What might be the challenges of this kind of work?

Research Assistant – Galapagos National Park, Ecuador

We are looking for a research assistant with a background in science. You must be physically fit, capable of working outside in extreme weather and available to work flexible hours. Salary depending on experience. Accommodations provided.

10.3 B **LISTEN FOR MAIN IDEA** Listen to the conversation and answer the questions.

1 What are the woman and man waiting for?

____

2 What are they both a little worried about?

____

3 What are they both positive about?

____

10.4 C **LISTEN FOR SPECIFIC INFORMATION** Listen to Jonathan's interview and complete the application form with one or two words in each blank.

10.5 D **LISTEN TO REGISTER** Jonathan used different registers to speak to Antonia and, later, to Dr. Ramsey. Listen to some extracts. In each case, decide how Jonathan could say the same thing in a different register.

1 _______________

2 _______________

3 _______________

4 _______________

10.6 E Now listen to how Jonathan says similar things in a different register and check your answers to Exercise D.

F **REFLECT** Think about the answers to these questions.

1 What are the most difficult things about living in an isolated place?

2 Do you frequently change register in your own language? Why?

Research Assistant – Galapagos National Park

Name	:	Jonathan Wheeler
Qualification(s)	:	Degree in [1] _______________
Studied at	:	University of [2] _______________ Anglia
Relevant experience	:	

- [3] _______________ months working for Nature Trust on the Isle of Skye
- Field trip: Northumberland, studying [4] _______________ of various species of birds
- Field trip: Forest of Dean, studying breeding habits of native [5] _______________
- Practical skills: maintenance work – fixing fences and maintenance of [6] _______________

In the space provided, please state what appeals to you about the Galapagos National Park:

I think it's essential that we [7] _______________ nature as much as we can and, for me, this is a great opportunity to study a relatively unspoiled area. I think that tourism and industry are [8] _______________ so much of nature. It's vital that we conduct [9] _______________ while we still can, in the hope that we can protect wildlife.

WRITING

A Read the title of the essay. What are some of the pros and cons of tourism?

B Read the whole essay and answer the questions.

1. What is the writer's opinion of tourism?
2. What arguments does the writer use to support their opinions?
3. Does the writer mention any positive aspects of mass tourism?

C **USING COUNTER-ARGUMENTS AND REBUTTALS** Read the essay again and answer the questions.

1. Which paragraph includes examples of counter-arguments (i.e. stating an opposing position) and rebuttals (i.e. stating why you believe an argument is incorrect)?
2. What is the counter-argument and what is the rebuttal? Does the rebuttal directly answer the counter-argument?
3. What phrases are used to introduce the counter-argument and rebuttal?

WRITING PRACTICE

A **PREPARE** Read this essay title and write some notes on each of the points.

> Do shopping malls have a positive or negative impact on local communities?

- job opportunities
- prices
- convenience
- local businesses
- environmental impact

B **PLAN** You are going to write a persuasive essay in answer to the task above.

- Organize your notes from Exercise A into an appropriate structure for a persuasive essay.
- Use a counter-argument and rebuttal in the third or fourth paragraph.

C **WRITE** Write your essay in 220–260 words.

Does tourism have a POSITIVE OR NEGATIVE IMPACT?

1 Cheap air travel has opened up the world to more and more people and few countries are unaffected by mass tourism. Many argue that this is a good thing – that it promotes understanding of different cultures and makes international connections. However, I believe that in the long term, tourism has a negative impact, spoiling the very places it promotes.

2 First, there is the environmental damage mass tourism brings with it. Ugly hotels built near traditional architecture, increased traffic congestion bringing pollution, more litter and waste to dispose of; the list goes on. Even if tourists do behave responsibly, sheer numbers can cause problems, such as damage to ancient buildings and monuments.

3 Mass tourism can also damage the heart and soul of a tourist destination by making it just like any other vacation resort. Cultural history and heritage are reduced to a spectacle for visitors, and tourists often lack respect for local traditions and culture, ignoring local codes of behavior and upsetting the local community. It leads, therefore, to the opposite of promoting understanding between cultures.

4 There is an argument that mass tourism has a beneficial impact because it brings in money and creates new jobs. Hotels, stores and restaurants all need staffing. While this is true up to a point, it should be remembered that many of these jobs are low-skilled and are often seasonal and insecure with no benefits such as pensions, sick pay or healthcare. Also, most of the tourism industry is owned by big foreign companies: they get the profits, while local businesses receive little benefit.

5 In conclusion, the long-term effects of mass tourism are largely negative. It can impact negatively on the environment, damage or destroy local cultures and traditions, the jobs it provides are insecure and short-lived, and local businesses suffer while the profits go to foreign corporations.

UNIT 1

Lesson 1.4, Listening, Exercise B
1.4 **W = Woman M = Man**

W: Have you watched this year's GenZ Round-up?

M: No, what's that?

W: It's a video series that the video site GenZ creates at the end of every year. It has – like – well, everything that's happened in the last 12 months.

M: OK. It sounds interesting. Like – a round-up of the year?

W: Exactly. They did the first one in 2012, and that kind of set a trend. They've been doing one every year since. Each year has a slightly different title though, for example, 2016 was 'GenZ Round-up: The Best of 2016' and 2017 was 'GenZ Round-up: Here's 2017'.

M: And this year's?

W: Well, here's the thing. This year's was really bad. Everybody hated it and it got really bad reviews!

M: Why?

W: A lot of viewers said that it didn't include enough content creators – you know – the people who actually make the site what it is. Also, it included a lot of celebrity endorsements and people thought that was a bit cheesy.

M: Hey! I've had a great idea! Why don't we make our own 'Round-up' video?

W: Actually, a lot of people are doing just that – making their own videos.

M: OK. Let's do it! You're really media-savvy. What should we include?

W: As a general rule, we should include all the latest trends, the most popular videos – the ones that went viral, for instance, and everyone watched.

M: Like when that TV announcer fell off his chair live on air a few years ago?

W: Exactly!

M: What else?

W: It's a good idea to include top news stories from the previous year, too. I mean, the really big ones that everybody talked about. You don't need to include a lot of detail – maybe just an image of a person who was in the headlines with some bright colors or special effects.

M: Do you know how to do that?

W: Yes, don't worry. It's not difficult. I have a program on my computer that does it. The trick is to keep the video moving at a really fast pace and to use a variety of different media. For example, we could add in some animation – clips from superhero movies or popular cartoons.

M: This is going to be great! What about those little – what do you call them – you know – those photos with the funny text that everyone shares and passes around?

W: Memes?

M: Yes, that's it.

W: You're right. We definitely have to include last year's most popular memes. I know – let's ask our friends to tell us their favorites, and those are the ones we'll include.

M: Good idea.

W: There's one thing this video really needs and that's influencers.

M: What do you mean?

W: Influencers – they don't watch videos or 'like' the content, they *are* the content, they *set* the trends. I'm talking about GenZ personalities and vloggers – like Daisy Trekker, for instance.

M: What is a vlogger exactly?

W: Oh, come on! You must know what a vlogger is.

M: Well, kind of …

W: Basically, they record video diaries of different things – sports, playing computer games, testing new products or just their ordinary lives.

M: So, they're like … trendsetters?

W: Exactly. It's worth including their videos because everybody loves them and then maybe people will watch *our* video. Generally speaking, we have to include stuff that's *relevant*. It has to be new – or newish anyway. And we can't forget to include some clips from fashion and beauty vlogs – those are really popular, too. My favorite is Bonella – she has more than 11 million subscribers.

M: That's amazing! So, what are we waiting for? Let's get started.

W: OK. I'll go and get my laptop …

UNIT 2

Lesson 2.4, Listening, Exercise C
2.3 **P = Presenter R = Ruth**

P: Architecture may not be the first discipline which springs to mind when somebody mentions 'art', but some of the most famous artists in the world – like Michelangelo and Raphael – were architects as well as painters. In the modern world, architects like Frank Lloyd Wright and Le Corbusier command world-wide respect and admiration.

Today, we're going to be looking at the work of Frank Gehry, a Canadian-American architect whose designs include the Walt Disney Concert Hall in the US and the Guggenheim Museum in Bilbao, Spain. Here to tell us about him is art historian Ruth Butler. Good morning, Ruth, thanks for joining us.

R: Good morning. Thanks for inviting me.

P: Frank Gehry has become so famous that he's almost a household name. He's been referred to by some commentators as a 'starchitect'. Tell us a little bit more about the man.

R: Of course, Nick. A starchitect is a reference to his kind of – well, his 'star' status in the world of architecture, but actually, he doesn't like that term at all. He's proud of his work and highly respected, but he doesn't like the idea of celebrity status. So … Gehry was born in Canada. His family was of Polish origin and his name was originally Frank *Goldberg* – he changed his name to Gehry while he was studying at the Southern California School of Architecture.

P: Tell us about his early career. Was he immediately successful?

R: No, not really. Like most great artists, he went through difficult times before he made it big. After finishing his studies – he also studied city planning at Harvard University – he worked for a number of different firms and tried his hand at furniture design, as well as renovating his own home in a way which would become – well, the style that he's now known for.

P: His signature style, you could say?

R: Yes, that's right.

P: Tell us a little bit about that.

R: Well, his early work was a reaction against the modernist buildings of the 60s and 70s which were springing up all over the cities of America. There was a lot of glass, a lot of sharp angles and forms which reflected advances in science, and industry and technology of the period. Gehry wanted to emphasize the human angle, and of course contextual integrity was very important to him.

P: I think you'll have to explain that to our listeners, Ruth.

R: Yes, of course. The 'context' of a building is its location, the other buildings and structures around it, the immediate environment I would say. It was important to Gehry that his work – his buildings – reflected their surroundings, the historical or social aspects of where they were – the context if you will. So … um … back to his style … His style is very 'sculptural' you know. He uses materials and forms shapes and structures almost in the way a sculptor might. He's probably best known for his use of unusual materials and for the creation of bold and unconventional shapes through the use of those materials.

P: We have some photos of Gehry's work here in the studio.

R: Yes, this one is an excellent example of what I'm talking about. This building is known as the Dancing House and it's in Prague in the Czech Republic. The building looks almost as if it's moving from side to side like two dancers. This is very different from the traditional lines and forms of previous buildings.

P: Awesome!

R: During the 80s and 90s, he was offered commissions throughout the world: Prague – as we've seen – Spain, the US, Germany. And his reputation just grew and grew from then on really. Arguably his most iconic building is the Guggenheim Museum in Spain which you mentioned at the beginning of the program, Nick. Visitors to this, and other buildings of Gehry, have commented that the space he's created inside is more impressive than the objects it was designed to house.

P: It does look like – well – like a sculpture in its own right.

R: Exactly. It's really an architectural landmark – literally and metaphorically.

P: Thank you, Ruth, for this insight into the life and work of one of the world's greatest living architects.

R: I just hope it inspires some of your listeners to read and learn more about him, Nick. I think they'll find his work fascinating.

UNIT 3

3.3 Lesson 3.4, Listening, Exercise B
J = Joanna S = Steven R = Rachel

J: Hi, Steven! Welcome to the World Aid Expo. I'm Joanna.

S: Hello. Um … how do you know my name?

J: Your name badge?

S: Oh, yes of course. Silly me! Um, hi Joanna.

J: So, Steven. I bet you know a lot about important social and environmental issues, right? You look like a well-educated person. Are you a student?

S: Yes, I am actually. I must say I didn't expect this much from the Expo, but I was so wrong. It's fascinating – all the different stalls, a lot of information, new ideas …

J: Absolutely. It's probably *the* most important event on the calendar, definitely the most interesting! Hey, listen … I just get a feeling about you. You're a kind-hearted person, aren't you? I bet you're someone who actually helps other people. You genuinely care about their problems, their situations. Am I right?

S: Well, yes, I …

J: To be honest, there are so many visitors this year, but I haven't approached them because I don't feel that I've seen anyone … who's, well, who's *genuine*. Somebody who feels as passionately about helping others as I do – as our organization does.

S: What does your organization do exactly?

J: I'm *so* glad you asked. We work with local communities in Tanzania – a beautiful country … really, you're going to *love* it when you go there … We work with schools, women's groups, youth and community groups. This year, we're building a library in the town of Arusha. You can see Mount Kilimanjaro from there. Can you visualize that?

S: Yes, it sounds amazing.

J: It's *absolutely* stunning! And *you* can be part of our vision, Steven. We really need volunteers to come out to Tanzania and help with building the library.

S: Um … don't you need special skills – you know – to … um … build a, well, a building? I'm afraid I don't know much about bricklaying or concrete or electrics or anything.

J: That's not a problem! Not a problem at all. I just know that your passion and your commitment are what we need on this project.

S: Well, I don't know. What would it involve exactly?

J: You fly out to Tanzania – we organize one-week and two-week trips. You'll be staying in local accommodations – nothing fancy, but I'm sure you won't mind that. You'll meet our local coordinator who'll allocate a workplace to you. Maybe we'll even organize trips to local sights. Sounds a little too good to be true, doesn't it?

S: Um … it sounds interesting.

J: Of course, this *is* a volunteer project, so obviously you won't be paid.

S: Oh, of course not. I wouldn't expect that.

J: What do you say? Are you interested?

S: Yes, I'm definitely …

J: That's fantastic! I bet you're good at creative writing, aren't you? When you come home again, we'd love you to write about your experience.

S: Well, I *am* quite …

J: Amazing, I'll put you down for the writing! Excellent. Of course, there are some expenses. We don't want local people having to contribute to the cost of volunteers' food. So, we ask for a donation from you of $500 for that – that's per week.

S: Yes, of course.

J: And then there are the flights – just $980. We arrange everything, don't worry. And we have some really good news this year – no administration costs, the organization is covering that side of things. So, nothing to pay there. How good is that?

S: Do you have an application form?

J: Yes, absolutely. If you'd like to go over there and speak to the woman in the green jacket – she's our team leader. She'll give you a form to fill out and you can discuss payment with her.

S: Thanks so much Joanna. I'll see you in a little while. I'll come back when I've completed the application.

J: Hi, Rachel! Welcome to the World Aid Expo. I'm Joanna.

R: Oh hi. Wow … how do you know my name?

UNIT 4

Lesson 4.4, Listening, Exercise B
4.3 **L = Leah N = Nadia C = Charles**

L: In today's *Looking further*, we're asking, 'Just how smart are human beings?' To help me answer this, I have two guests in the studio: Charles Bragg from the London Animal Rights Center and Professor Nadia Abbas. Good morning to you both.

N: Hello.

C: Hi.

L: Nadia – what's your view? Are human beings really the most intelligent creatures on the planet?

N: As a lecturer in anthropology, I would have to answer 'yes'. For many years, scientists and academics have carried out experiments which conclude that we are indeed the most intelligent species on the planet. We can understand abstract concepts and use an accumulation of knowledge to manipulate our environment, and of course our use of language is second to none. But perhaps most important of all is our ability to reason – to have the kind of discussion which we're having right now!

C: But what you're saying has been 'proved' historically is actually just an *assumption* by scientists. Just because we've always believed something doesn't necessarily make it true. I genuinely don't think scientists can be trusted on this issue because they, quite simply, never question their own opinions and assumptions.

N: Well, I agree with you on that point Charles – of course our views and beliefs change over time – but, nevertheless, the vast body of research proves that humans are the most intelligent species.

C: But Nadia – experiments are a reflection of the people carrying them out. Much of the research you're talking about was skewed by those scientists' existing views of human intelligence and was designed to support those views. When people have tried to analyze animal intelligence, they've always focused on a strictly human definition of intelligence. I mean – so what if a squirrel can't count to ten? Squirrels don't need to be able to count to ten!

N: I agree in part with what you're saying, Charles. Some of the qualities which we regard as essentially human – reasoning, language and so on – are just one *form* of intelligence. In fact, in some ways, it's perhaps meaningless to judge animal intelligence by human standards. But …

C: Well, there you are! It's a question of different degrees of intelligence. I mean – think about dogs. I was taking my dog out for a walk last week and I was amazed that while most of the people were listening to headphones or not talking at all, he was picking up on the smells that other dogs had left. If that's not evidence that dogs have equally complex forms of communication, I don't know what is. My dog is very good at communicating his demands to me and getting me to do what he wants.

N: Well, of course, but that's a matter of conditioning. There's no comparison though between the way in which a dog communicates basic needs and the incredibly complex systems of verbal and written communication which humans have developed over thousands of years.

C: Well, let me give you another example. We know that killer whales have a rich and complex language. In fact, I was watching a TV documentary about it just last night. Dolphins have individual names based on whistle signals. That's proof that animals can communicate just as well as humans do.

N: OK, I think you're confused about what I'm saying. But let's leave language aside for the moment. The way in which we are able to accumulate knowledge and use that knowledge to manipulate our environment is key. This ability has even allowed us to send a spacecraft to Mars.

C: But that's precisely my point! Animals don't want or need to go to Mars! But they *also* have incredibly complex systems which they use on an everyday basis – I mean … humans have traveled to the moon, but have they perfected a system of echolocation such as bats use? No!

N: I do agree that some research is leading us to question our assumptions about animal intelligence, but this *still* doesn't allow us to conclude that animals are equally intelligent. Let me give you an example. If we compare chimps and humans, when it comes to tasks which require 'social learning', like watching somebody else completing a task and then copying their behavior, human toddlers are way ahead of chimpanzees.

C: Yes, but …

L: Charles, Nadia – I think this debate could probably go on for hours, but that's all we have time for today, so we're going to have to leave it there.

UNIT 5

Lesson 5.4, Listening, Exercise B

5.3 J = John A = Andrea

J: Today, we're talking to psychologist Andrea Preston about the consequences of too much time spent gaming and online. And we're also asking what can be done about it. So, Andrea, should we be worried?

A: Hi John. Well, as worried as we are about other forms of compulsive behavior, yes. Spending too much time playing video games is a serious issue for many people.
Of course, there's a difference between someone who enjoys video games and even the more avid gamer who spends most of their free time on gaming. What we're talking about here is when gaming gets in the way of everyday life.

J: Right! With two children at home, I think I might know what you mean. But at what point does it become a problem?

A: Well, signs to watch out for are preferring to spend time alone in front of a screen instead of spending time with family and friends. In some cases, gaming can interfere with everyday tasks like washing, eating and sleeping.
I guess when you have some countries introducing laws to regulate the amount of time young people can spend playing online video games, you know you should be paying attention.

J: I guess so. But that does seem like a step too far. Should governments be calling the shots?

A: Hmm … for some it does seem like an obvious solution. Governments could pass laws preventing players from participating in online games for more than a certain period of time. Problem solved. But the amount of time spent playing games may in fact be a symptom of deeper psychological issues. We should actually attempt to help gamers create personal boundaries and balance around gaming rather than banning or restricting by law. But more importantly, we should treat the underlying causes of a person's reliance on such games.

J: Surely all this comes down to parenting, don't you think?

A: Well, it depends. Conventional wisdom might say that parents aren't being hard enough on this issue, you know, by setting clear boundaries with their children. But there are two things we need to be clear on. First, the problem doesn't just affect younger gamers. We're talking about adults as well. Second, while yes of course friends and family can play a positive role, being stricter and making rules won't necessarily get to the root of the problem.

J: So, what is at the root?

A: There are two things that I think usually get missed in the discussion. First of all, we need to be clear that games tap into very human desires. We crave challenges and games are set so they are never too easy or difficult. Games also tap into our desire for rewards.

J: I have to admit that's what keeps me playing my children's games. Usually when they're not around!

A: You're not alone John. But there's more. It would be a mistake to ignore the social aspect of online games – after all, for many, gaming is also a form of social media. Many gamers feel a strong sense of belonging in their online communities, despite the fact that they will probably never meet in real life.

J: So, you're saying we need to recognize that games fulfill specific needs that we all have.

A: Yes, well put! Parents and friends of gamers should understand that. It's not about telling someone they can't do something. They should encourage gamers to replace the positive feelings they get through gaming with things like physical exercise. And if it's a serious problem, they should encourage the gamer to see a doctor or health professional.

J: So, it seems we can have too much of a good thing after all! Andrea, thanks so much for joining us.

A: Thanks for having me John.

UNIT 6

Lesson 6.4, Listening, Exercise B

6.3

Perhaps one of the most well-known figures in modern British history is the explorer, Robert Falcon Scott. Tragically, he is not famous for his achievement, but for his failure. Scott headed an expedition whose goal was to reach the South Pole before anyone else. On January 17, 1912, Scott, with four companions, finally reached the South Pole, only to discover that a Norwegian party, led by Roald Amundsen, had beaten them to it – by just 34 days. Scott and his men died on their journey home.

Lesson 6.4, Listening, Exercise C

6.4

From *the* mid-19th century, a number of expeditions had traveled to Antarctica to try and map its extent and find out more about the wildlife and plantlife of this unknown territory. The men who undertook these journeys suffered terrible hardship; sickness, injury, hunger *and* cold were part of their everyday experience. Every single item which the explorers needed *had* to be transported by ship. Then the provisions had to be carried across *the* ice. These included tents, sleeping bags, building materials, food for men and animals, heating oil, bedding, clothing *and* scientific equipment.

Both Scott and Amundsen set out for *their* final trek to the South Pole within a few weeks of each other. Amundsen's journey *went* smoothly, and his entire team returned safe and sound a month later. In contrast, as *we* have already learned, Scott and his companions were beaten to their goal and ultimately lost their lives. *What* factors led to these *two* totally different results?

Amundsen's only goal was to reach the South Pole before anyone else. In contrast, Scott's expedition *was* meant to be a voyage of scientific discovery and he put together a large scientific team including a zoologist, meteorologist, geologists and biologists. Some experts believe *that* Amundsen's clear focus on a single goal was key to his success.

Scott planned to use a mixture of transportation – motor sleds, pony and *dog* sleds and 'man-hauling', in other words, the men themselves pulling sleds. *The* first motor sled broke down before they even set out, the second fell through the ice, and the third broke down shortly afterwards. The ponies were totally unsuited *to* the climate and the heavy work and they all died of cold and hunger. The dogs *were* better-suited to the conditions, but they were worked so hard, and fed so little, that they too died eventually. By contrast, Amundsen's expedition relied entirely *on the best Antarctic transportation at the time*: dog sleds. *He* hired experienced dog drivers and made sure his dogs were fed properly and only traveled for short distances every day.

Amundsen embarked *on* his final trek to the Pole from a point much closer than Scott. Advance parties *marked* almost the entire length of the route with flags and frequent food depots which were clearly marked so that they could not be missed by the men in the mist and snow. Scott's *food* depots were located far less frequently. Scott's team frequently lost *their* way and often had difficulty locating these. *The* food which Scott provided was not adequate for his team's needs. Some of the group were *suffering* from 'scurvy', a condition caused by lack of vitamins which slowly but surely weakens physical strength. Amundsen had taken care of providing enough food, including *a* specially designed mixture which contained vitamins. He supplemented this diet with *fresh seal meat*.

While Scott's story has become a legend of British history, Amundsen's *clear* thinking, expert planning, training and experience meant that he succeeded in his expedition.

UNIT 7

Lesson 7.4, Listening, Exercise B
7.3 **C = Caroline T = Thomas**

C: Welcome to *Beyond Brave* with me Caroline Spencer. Today, Thomas Bennett is here to talk to us about tightrope walking. Why has it become such a popular topic recently?

T: Well, what has brought it to public attention is the exploits of contemporary performers such as Nik Wallenda and Philippe Petit.

C: Tell us something about these two extraordinary people.

T: You might say that Nik Wallenda has tightrope walking in his blood. He represents the latest generation of a family who have been circus performers since the 1700s. It was his great-grandfather, Karl Wallenda, who perfected circus acts including the human pyramid, as well as high-wire walking and cycling. He was killed attempting to walk between two skyscrapers in 1978. That's probably why Nik has devoted his life to tightrope walking. In 2011, he successfully completed the same walk in honor of his great-grandfather.

C: Incredible! I find him a very charismatic figure. But he also uses the power of the media to his advantage, doesn't he?

T: Oh yes. I think it's partly as a result of his relationship with TV networks that his exploits have reached such a wide audience. It's been estimated that 16 million people watched his walk across Niagara Falls on live television.

C: You mentioned another great tightrope artist, Philippe Petit, earlier? His accomplishments were made into a film, weren't they?

T: That's right. *Man on Wire* won the Oscar for best documentary in 2008.

C: It's a somewhat obscure thing to make a documentary about, isn't it?

T: Well, yes it is. And to be honest, if the film hadn't been made, I don't think there would have been so much interest in the whole idea of tightrope walking. The film tells the story of Petit's 1974 high-wire walk between the Twin Towers of New York's World Trade Center. His incredibly daring – and I might add illegal – achievement was the focus of the film.

C: What do you mean 'illegal'?

T: Well, because the stunt was so incredibly dangerous. I mean … the guy was going to walk across a wire just two and a half centimeters wide, across a distance of nearly 40 meters which was … wait for it … more than 400 meters above the ground. If anything had gone wrong, well – the consequences would have been utterly dreadful. And New York City didn't want to be associated with the possibly tragic result of such an event, so obviously they never gave Petit permission to carry out the stunt. So, the preparations had to be done in secret – examining the site, installing the equipment, the timings, everything. It was a bit like one of those classic bank heists you see in the movies! He and his team had to get up the two towers in secret, fire a guiding rope from one tower to the other with a bow and arrow …

C: A bow and arrow?!

T: That's right! And then Petit crossed – not just once, but four times – backwards and forwards across the wire while a crowd of thousands gathered below and watched in terrified astonishment. After he'd completed the feat, he was arrested by waiting police officers. The police released him pretty soon afterwards though.

C: And there's been a more recent movie, hasn't there?

T: The 2015 movie *The Wire* is a biographical drama of the same story. It's thanks to this that younger people are taking a renewed interest.

UNIT 8

Lesson 8.4, Listening, Exercise B
8.3 **S = Scott A = Angela**

S: Today, we're going to be broadcasting live from a space training facility in Germany. With me is scientist and researcher, Angela Schneider.

A: Good morning, Scott. It's a pleasure to be able to talk to you and your listeners.

S: So, what do you do exactly, Angela?

A: I'm a nutritionist by training and over the last few years, I've specialized in research into the effects of a zero-gravity environment on the human body. Good nutrition is critical for human health and of course this is true for those traveling in space, too. It's important that astronauts have a specially designed diet which gives them exactly the right number of calories which they need to do their work and the correct balance of vitamins and nutrients for optimum performance and well-being.

S: What problems do astronauts face in terms of their physical health?

A: Astronauts are known to lose bone density during any extended stay in space, and this means they are at an increased risk of bone fractures once they return to Earth, so we've been looking at ways of dealing with that problem. New diet programs include vitamin D and calcium supplements. In addition, astronauts follow a program of resistance training, which has been proved to be very effective in preventing bone density loss.

S: What other nutrients are important?

A: That's an interesting question, Scott. Another essential nutrient that we've been studying is iron. As I'm sure you and your listeners know, iron deficiency in the blood can lead to anemia – where you don't have enough red blood cells. Some of the symptoms of anemia are fatigue, dizziness and headaches. So, we were focusing on making sure that our astronauts had enough iron in their diet, but we've come to the surprising conclusion that actually, they end up with an *excessive* amount of iron in their blood as a result of living in space for long periods of time. So, we're looking to actually reduce the iron content in the foods which we provide for our crews.

S: So … less of the spinach eh?

A: That's right! And as well as these vital scientific aspects, we have to make the food palatable for the men and women who are working in space. In the past, some astronauts have complained that the food – in the shape of bite-sized cubes, powders and freeze-dried foodstuffs – was unappetizing and bland. Today, we offer foods which are cutting-edge in terms of the latest scientific research, but which are also … well, really tasty actually.

S: Can you give us some examples of what an astronaut might expect to find on the menu here?

A: Um … let me see. Duck breast with capers, lobster, chocolate cake …

S: No! Really?

A: Yes, really. We've teamed up with chefs to come up with really delicious dishes. We even have a 'special occasion' menu for birthdays or when there's a change of crew.

S: That's amazing! Well, Angela. It's been absolutely fascinating to talk to you. Thanks so much.

A: Thank *you*!

UNIT 9

Lesson 9.4, Listening, Exercise B
9.3 **R = Rob S = Sandy C = Cassie**

R: All right, Sandy? What's up?

S: Hi Rob. This is my friend Cassie.

R: Hi, Cassie. Nice to meet you. How are you doing?

C: Good, thanks.

R: So … you just moved here, Cassie?

C: No, actually. I've lived here for … let me see … for four years.

R: So how come you don't go to our school?

C: I go to a Steiner school.

S: How cool is that? Like – *so* awesome!

R: Um … well, I don't mean to be rude or anything, but … why's that 'awesome' exactly?

S: Cos it's you know … it's really *unique* and stuff. Go on Cassie. Tell Rob all about your school.

C: No, it's OK. You probably don't want to hear about it anyway.

R: Yes … no … I mean, course I want to hear about it.

C: Well, the … you know … philosophy behind the school is that education is about more than just passing exams and learning a ton of stuff.

S: That's *so* true!

C: So, the idea is that you develop as a, well, a whole person. The school is supposed to develop your artistic and practical skills as well as your intellectual ones. Probably *the* most important thing is imagination. You learn to be a responsible … human being.

R: Yeah, right!

S: Be quiet, Rob!

C: Yeah, sounds silly I know …

S: No, no. Not at all. Don't take any notice of Rob. *I* think it sounds fantastic. I mean … at our school there's a huge amount of pressure on us to study and pass exams.

R: Hang on. You're right – there *is* a lot of pressure, but I mean – like – I'd be bummed if I didn't get the grades I want to go to college. So, there *is* a reason behind the pressure.

S: Yeah, but it's too much. Even the teachers are under pressure. If we don't get good exam grades, then they get into a lot of trouble. These inspectors come around every semester and check *everything*.

R: Anyway, tell us some more about *your* school. Is it one of those places where you can, you know, do anything you want? Mess around all day? Not go to lessons.

C: No, it's not like that at all. Maybe I'm not explaining it well. It's more to do with *who you are*. For instance, we're not in classes according to our age – everybody lumped in together just because their birthdays happen to be in the same year. We're grouped according to our interests and stage of development. Each person is treated differently, and you can learn at your own pace and in a way that suits you.

S: Do you have assembly in the morning, like we do?

C: No, we start the day with group exercises, recitals and songs. It's supposed to put you in the mood to learn – forget any negative thoughts, get in the right space to really focus. Then we have a two-hour lesson which is always based on one topic. It's not like – first, math, then geography, then English–like most other schools.

R: So, why's it called 'Steiner' anyway?

C: Rudolf Steiner was the founder of the whole … philosophy … the system. He was this Austrian guy who lived in … I'm not sure … at the beginning of the 20th century anyway. Today, there are hundreds of Steiner schools all over the world.

S: I think you're so lucky, Cassie. I wish I could go to your school.

UNIT 10

Lesson 10.4, Listening, Exercise B
10.3 **J = Jonathan A = Antonia**

J: Hiya. Jonathan. How you doing?

A: All right? I'm Antonia. You here for the interview?

J: Yep. Been waiting long?

A: Nah – 'bout five minutes. There's tea and coffee here. D'you want something?

J: Yeah, I wouldn't mind a cup.

A: Got it.

J: Great.

A: So … we're both up for the same job?

J: Yeah. You done anything like this before?

A: No. You?

J: Well, I've studied – conservation I mean, so I've done a lot of field trips and stuff. I spent last summer working on the Isle of Skye in Scotland. But the Galapagos …

A: What? I've never been to either. I guess you have a better idea of what the job will involve – if you lived in Skye?

J: Well, it's a commitment. It's somewhat cut off. I know you can fly into Puerto Ayora and then take a boat, but it's expensive and sometimes, the water taxis don't run. That's my only hesitation … It's a bit of an isolated place to live all year round.

A: You can say that again. It bothers me a little bit, too, if I'm honest. I heard they have a tendency to cancel flights and boats because of bad weather. You know I, um, I'm not sure how I feel about that.

J: Yeah. You're right. The job looks great though. Everything I love doing. But I have no desire to be stuck there!

A: Yes, what a great thing to spend your time doing. You know … looking on the bright side.

Lesson 10.4, Listening, Exercise C
10.4 **D = Dr. Ramsey J = Jonathan**

D: Jonathan Wheeler?

J: Hello Dr. Ramsey. How do you do?

D: Good morning, Jonathan. Would you like to come on through? Can I get you anything? Tea? Coffee?

J: A glass of water would be great, thank you.

D: Please have a seat. So … you've just graduated. Tell me more!

J: Yes, that's right. I have a degree in environmental science from the University of East Anglia and actually have practical experience from several field trips.

D: And I see that you worked with the Nature Trust on the Isle of Skye last year. So, you've worked in a remote area before?

J: Yes, that's correct. I was there for two months. It was fascinating.

D: And your field trips … one was studying birds in Northumberland …

J: Yes, we studied their natural habitats.

D: And you also went to the Forest of Dean.

J: Yes … to study the breeding patterns of the deer that live there.

D: Well, that's all good experience. How did you find the physical side of things? The post requires you to be physically fit – out in all weather – that kind of thing.

J: Oh, I like hard work. I've done a lot of fencing, maintaining paths … that kind of thing.

D: OK. And I see here at the bottom of your form that you're very much committed to the environment and nature – you want to preserve it, you say here.

J: Yes, I think a lot of things are endangering so much of the environment – for instance, things like tourism and industry – and it's happening very quickly. So, while there is still time, I think we should carry out research and … hopefully … we will protect the wildlife we have – keep it for future generations.

D: One last question. What attracted you to this job in particular?

J: I really feel that the job is an ideal opportunity for me, and it involves everything that I enjoy doing.

Answer key

1.1 Dress for success

VOCABULARY

A

1 follow **2** casual **3** outfit **4** set **5** sportswear
6 uniform **7** stands **8** gear **9** oversized **10** baggy

B

1. wind you up
2. snapped up
3. catches your eye
4. throwing money down the drain
5. make a seamless transition
6. in the long run
7. off-the-rack
8. tailor-made
9. are on a tight budget
10. for peanuts

GRAMMAR

A

1 c **2** b **3** a **4** f **5** e **6** d

B

1. it
2. how
3. that
4. not
5. was
6. why
7. where
8. What

C

1. the problem of
2. The fact that
3. How she spends her money
4. do not/don't mind wearing

1.2 Trendsetting

GRAMMAR

A

1. as quickly as
2. dramatically
3. latest
4. louder
5. a higher
6. Easily the most
7. a considerably higher
8. great
9. deeper

B

1 c **2** d **3** b **4** f **5** a **6** e **7** h **8** g

VOCABULARY

A

1. hyper-influential
2. tech-savvy
3. waterproof
4. amateurish
5. disaster-prone
6. undelete
7. user-friendly
8. super-lucky

B

1. heat-resistant
2. largish
3. spammy
4. rethink
5. cheesy
6. unmuted
7. idiot-proof
8. ultra-/super-/hyper-cautious

PRONUNCIATION

A

1. He's suggesting one solution, but there are others.
   He's suggesting one solution, is that the best he can do?
2. They told me to work on this project, so that's what I'm doing.
   They said the same to me, and that's what I am doing.
3. He suggested that the biggest problem is overseas sales.
   But you don't realize that the biggest problem is overseas sales.
4. I can do it; the question is whether I want to do it.
   I can do it, too, but I don't know when.
5. Do you think this will be a problem?
   Without question, this will be a problem.

C

1. I was determined not to say anything that could get me in trouble.
2. Contrary to what you said, I do enjoy gardening.
3. Bill got the contract and a promotion, so he's happy.

1.3 Reading

READING

B

1 e **2** c **3** a **4** b **5** d

C

1. increasing
2. friendly
3. rare
4. unlikely
5. exciting, unusual
6. open, outgoing

D

1 d **2** f **3** a **4** c **5** e **6** b

1.4 Listening

LISTENING

B

2, 3, 6, 7, 9

C

1 round-up
2 reviews
3 (TV) presenter
4 Special effects
5 animation
6 friends
7 vlogger
8 new/newish/relevant

1.5 Write a blog post

WRITING

A

Possible answers

1 format, repetition of keywords/phrases, etc
2 layout, pictures, font style, etc
3 publish relevant content, use keywords, update your content regularly, etc

B

1 c 2 d 3 a 4 b

C

1 successful, blog, post, blog post
2 By structuring it well and using headings, the search engine will pick up on key topics and help improve your ranking. Also, being reader-friendly, it will attract more readers, and more readers means more clicks. This also helps to improve ranking.
3 Add links and more posts to your website.
4 'For more tips …', 'click on the icon below'.

WRITING PRACTICE

C

Model answer

4 FAQs about electric vehicles

If you are concerned about the environment and want motoring to be cheaper and safer, then electric vehicles (EVs) are the thing for you. As the trend for EVs grows, more and more people are getting interested. Here are answers to four of the most frequently asked questions (FAQs).

1 Are they really eco-friendly?

Yes, absolutely. They don't burn fuel, so there are no emissions. By not using gas or diesel, they are not adding to the gases that cause air pollution and contribute to global warming. Driving an EV substantially reduces your carbon footprint.

2 Are they economical?

Again, yes. Because you're not paying for gas to keep your EV running, you save a lot on fuel. Charging your EV could cost less than $1, depending on the type of vehicle. EVs are also cheaper to maintain. EV engines have far fewer parts that can go wrong than conventional cars, and they are easier to fix.

3 Are they safe?

EVs are no less safe than other cars. We're not talking about driverless cars – you're still in charge. However, if you do have an accident, you are safer in an EV as there is little chance of it catching fire.

4 What about performance?

EVs are often more roomy than conventional cars because they have smaller engines. They also provide a smoother drive than conventional cars. As the market has become bigger, EV performance levels have improved greatly. One charge can take you between 100 and 200 miles, and as more people buy EVs, there will be more charging stations all over the country.

EVs are growing in popularity and are here to stay. They are clean, safe and cheap to run. What's not to like?

For more information about electric vehicles, click on the link below.

2.1 The story behind it

VOCABULARY

A

1 g 2 b 3 c 4 h 5 d 6 a 7 e 8 f

B

1 groundbreaking
2 overrated
3 pretentious
4 hilarious
5 unconventional
6 thought-provoking
7 sensational
8 tedious

C

1 sensational
2 iconic
3 repetitive
4 appalling
5 underrated
6 acclaimed

GRAMMAR

A

1 was being prepared
2 called
3 was waiting
4 had been damaged
5 had had
6 were told
7 wasn't I informed
8 had been snowing

B

So – big day today. Important meeting with some clients so I had to get to the office early. I got up at five, had a quick cup of coffee and **left** the house at 5:20. I got half way to the office when I realized that I **had forgotten** my phone. Can you believe it? I **had driven / had been driving** for at least half an hour already, so I really didn't feel like going back, but I **had** no choice. So, that delayed me by about an hour. And when I finally got to the office, I **was given** a message that my boss wanted to see me urgently. I ran to her office. I could see through the glass door she **was talking** to my clients, who **had** already arrived. Oh no! Luckily, she wasn't annoyed and my clients were fine. The meeting went well, and by lunchtime, we **had** agreed on everything.

2.2 Creative people

VOCABULARY

A

1 wall **2** canvas **3** start **4** draw **5** fresh **6** bounce **7** run **8** state **9** trust **10** immerse

B

1 late **2** part **3** thick **4** self **5** highly **6** world **7** open **8** well

GRAMMAR

A

1 d **2** e **3** f **4** b **5** a **6** c

B

1 a **2** c **3** a **4** b **5** a **6** b **7** c **8** b

2.3 Reading

READING

A

Possible answers

These words are connected to the topic and appear in the text: engineer, bridge, proposal, railway, carriage, survey, overground, construction

C

1 (Great) Britain/The UK and France
2 Eurobridge
3 six years (from 1988 to 1994)

D

1 b **2** b **3** a

2.4 Listening

LISTENING

A

Positive: awesome; groundbreaking; iconic; sensational; thought-provoking
Negative: appalling; pretentious
Neither positive nor negative: unconventional

B

Possible answers

1 architect
2 extremely
3 modern/unconventional

D

1 world-wide respect
2 celebrity status
3 difficult times
4 surroundings / (immediate) environment / context
5 unusual materials
6 more impressive

2.5 Write a review

WRITING

B

a 5 **b** 1 **c** 3 **d** 2 **e** 4

C

1 c; Organized in such a way as to surprise and delight the visitor, the paintings are presented in an unusual fashion.
2 b; Monet, born in 1840, continued painting until the mid-1920s.
3 a; French Impressionist painter Monet painted Rouen Cathedral several times.

WRITING PRACTICE

C

Model answer

The Hayward Gallery, located in the Southbank Center in Central London, is world-famous for its exhibits of contemporary art. The current exhibit focuses on the work of David Shrigley. Best known as a cartoonist, Shrigley demonstrates his talents as a fine artist here.

There are 240 works on display in this exhibit: cartoons, of course, but also photographs, some of which could be called absurdist, sculptures and … other things. Well, what would you call a cookie nailed to a wall? Also, paintings, animations and an installation of a swarm of insects made out of black metal wire.

All this would seem to indicate that Shrigley has roots in surrealism, and some pieces bring Salvador Dali and Rene Magritte to mind. The insects in the installation seem to refer to the ants that recur in Dali's paintings and Magritte's bright green apple makes an appearance. He also likes to play with the relative size of things, with small things made large beyond any possible usefulness, such as a cup of tea.

This is not to say that he is just a follower or imitator. He has his own style, with a wacky sense of humor, absurd, surreal and sometimes dark. There are those who don't consider this serious art – whatever that is – but jokes can often get you closer to the truth than seriousness. If not closer.

Well worth a visit, this exhibit is mischievous and full of fun, and I bet you will find it hard not to laugh out loud in the hushed atmosphere of the art gallery.

3.1 Progressive design

VOCABULARY

A

1 emissions
2 carbon-neutral
3 offset
4 sustainable
5 over-exploitation
6 depletion
7 biodegradable
8 renewable

B

1 visualize
2 deepen
3 empty
4 purify
5 enable
6 simplify
7 broadens
8 strengthen

GRAMMAR

A

1 b **2** e **3** d **4** a **5** c

B

1 d **2** a **3** f **4** g **5** b **6** h **7** e **8** c

PRONUNCIATION

A

1 C **2** A **3** B **4** C **5** B **6** C

3.2 Better … or worse?

PRONUNCIATION

A and B

1 If you **rewrite** (verb) the essay without the **extracts** (noun), I **suspect** (verb) your score will **increase** (verb) because it has a lot of positive **attributes** (noun).
2 Ignoring his **protests** (noun), the judge **rejected** (verb) his appeal because his **conduct** (noun) had been so poor, but he was **transferred** (verb) to an open prison and he was **permitted** (verb) to have access to a computer.
3 We asked the singer what he **attributed** (verb) his success to, and he said that he had **progressed** (verb) in the business because he hadn't given up, even when he had been publicly **insulted** (verb) in the press.
4 I didn't like these computers at first, but now I'm a **convert** (noun) and I plan to do some **research** (noun) to find out if I can **upgrade** (verb) my own at a reasonable price.
5 The island doesn't have many **exports** (noun) and they **import** (verb) a lot of goods, so the prices are much higher after **transportation** (noun) costs have been added.
6 Reports **conflict** (verb) as to whether the **conflict** (noun) was started by ticket holders or the security guards.

GRAMMAR

A

1 Not only **was** Jake ~~was~~ a good businessman, but he was also a kind person.
2 No sooner had we arrived **than** ~~when~~ it started to rain.
3 By no means **is** this ~~is~~ over.
4 Under no circumstances **must** you ~~must~~ disturb me.
5 Not once **did** they **say** ~~said~~ thank you.
6 No way **am** I ~~am~~ ever going back there!
7 Only after I insisted **did/would they replace** ~~replaced they~~ the broken phone.
8 Not since I was a child **have** I ~~have~~ felt so excited.

B

1 Never/Not
2 sooner
3 only
4 do/would
5 after/when
6 neither/nor
7 no

VOCABULARY

A

1 do
2 seen
3 perpetuating
4 seize
5 set
6 achieve
7 made
8 bring

B

1 made
2 perpetuate
3 displayed
4 make
5 brought
6 seize
7 take
8 set

3.3 Reading

READING

C

Communications

Benefits: everyday ease of keeping in touch, long-term effects on business

Costs: loss of mental skills (e.g. memorization), loss of practical skills (such as mental arithmetic), may interfere with the whole learning process

Medicine

Benefits: seeing a doctor online, remote operations, improved healthcare, more effective drugs, longevity, early retirement (as an advantage)

Costs: the cost of research and the price of new medicines, the cumulative effects of increased longevity (money for pensions, care for older people) and the effect on the job market

Industry

Benefits: people no longer have to do boring jobs, efficiency, economic growth and the benefits it brings (e.g. social and engineering projects)

Costs: traditional skills are being lost, loss of jobs

3.4 Listening

LISTENING

B

1, 2, 4, 5, 7, 8, 10

C

1 leading question
2 exaggeration
4 leading question
5 exaggeration
7 personalization
8 exaggeration
10 leading question

D

1 F (He didn't expect as much but has been impressed.)
2 F (She says she hasn't spoken to many people this year.)
3 F (He will help to build a library.)
4 T
5 T
6 F (He says he doesn't expect to be paid.)
7 F (He won't have to pay administration costs.)
8 T

3.5 Write a persuasive email

WRITING

A

1 (probably) the college principal
2 the teaching staff
3 to persuade them to support his proposal of introducing interactive whiteboards to the classrooms / to ask them to reply stating their support

B

a 4 **b** 2 **c** 1; 5 **d** 3 **e** 4

WRITING PRACTICE

C

Model answer

Dear All,

I know how hard you have all worked to make a success of this start-up business. We have acquired an impressive client base for such a small and new business and it looks as if we're going to keep growing. However, looking ahead, I can see we might have some problems in the future with inadequate internet connectivity.

We all have an equal interest in the company and what I am about to propose may mean a cut in salary for all of us in the short term, but if we get fiber optic cables installed now, we will be winners in the long run. Rapid connectivity is essential in our business and fiber optic cables, as you know, provide a higher bandwidth than what we have now and can transmit data over longer distances.

What is important is that the upgrade will improve our efficiency and allow us to expand our business. Although it is expensive to install, because we are centrally located and other businesses nearby already have fiber optics, it will be easier and cheaper for us. I have attached a breakdown of the costs so you can see how much we have to reduce costs in other areas and for how long.

It would be a shame to see all your talent and skill frustrated by out-of-date technology. We have laid solid foundations and have a loyal client base, and I believe we are strong enough to face this issue. We're in this together.

You are all bright, hard-working and adventurous people, otherwise you wouldn't be here. So let's take the next step to making our business grow even stronger in the future.

Best regards,
Sam

4.1 Brain training

VOCABULARY

A

1 d **2** e **3** a **4** c **5** b **6** b **7** c

B

1 crossroads **2** backwards **3** wasted **4** tempered
5 defenseless **6** shed **7** cool **8** attack

GRAMMAR

A

1 b **2** b **3** a **4** a **5** c **6** a **7** b **8** a

B

1 were you to
2 Should you see
3 had I done
4 Suppose you were
5 Had they realized
6 Ask anyone and

4.2 Thinking and thought

VOCABULARY

A

1 conducted; experiments
2 demonstrates; norms
3 speculate
4 participants; conclude
5 hypothesize
6 findings

B

1 troubleshoot
2 eureka
3 common
4 eccentric
5 absent
6 curious
7 overthink
8 wishful

GRAMMAR

A

1 h **2** d **3** f **4** b **5** e **6** a **7** c **8** g

B

1 had
2 could
3 have
4 only
5 wishes
6 should
7 was/were
8 should

PRONUNCIATION

A

1 A **2** B **3** A **4** B **5** A **6** B

4.3 Reading

READING

C

1 A **2** B **3** A **4** A **5** B **6** B

4.4 Listening

LISTENING

B

Yes, all of them were mentioned.

C

1 Nadia **2** Charles **3** Nadia **4** Charles **5** Charles **6** Nadia

D

1 B **2** A **3** A

4.5 Write a report

WRITING

B

a 3 Results
b 5 Conclusion
c 2 Methods
d 1 Introduction
e 4 Discussion

C

Introduction: 'The study suggests that …'
Discussion: 'the study suggests that'; 'lifestyle changes might delay decline by several years'
Conclusion: 'we strongly believe that in …'; '… a change in lifestyle involving aerobic exercise and a healthy diet may improve cognitive function'

WRITING PRACTICE

C

Model answer

Introduction

This report describes a study that investigated whether a combined program of healthy eating, exercise and brain training could have an effect on cognitive function in older people. Experts agree that what is good for the heart, such as regular exercise and a healthy diet, is good for the brain.

Methods

One thousand participants aged between 60 and 70 took part in this two-year-long study. All participants were tested for cognitive function, weight and blood pressure at the start of the study and again at 6, 12 and 24 months. Participants were then randomly split into two groups. The control groups received regular advice only. The intervention group received an intensive program which comprised of diet, exercise and cognitive training.

Results

The study found that overall the scores in tests measuring cognitive function in the intervention group were 25% higher than the scores in the control group. In tests for executive function – the brain's ability to plan, organize, solve problems and make decisions – the intervention group scored 83% higher than the control group. It should be pointed out, however, that as with previous studies, the intervention group showed no improvement in memory.

Discussion

The researchers believe that the fact that 12% of the participants dropped out of the trial does not affect the results. They say their findings indicate that intervention is effective in treating the problems associated with aging and brain function. This research replicates the findings of the original study.

Conclusion

It can be concluded that a combined program of diet, planned exercise as well as 'brain training' is effective in improving age-related cognitive function.

5.1 21st century games

GRAMMAR

A

1 get
2 being
3 to go
4 to be
5 get
6 being
7 congratulated
8 got

B

1 am/'m always (being/getting) asked
2 had/'d been invited / was/got invited
3 had been chosen / was/got chosen
4 was being developed / had been developed
5 to be done
6 going to be made to
7 is/gets/was/got broken

PRONUNCIATION

A

1 Contract? What contract?
2 Really?
3 No way! Again?
4 Seriously?
5 Are you joking?
6 Yeah, right!

VOCABULARY

A

1 g
2 b
3 d
4 a
5 f
6 c
7 h
8 e

B

1 outsmarted
2 outplayed
3 outweigh
4 outrun
5 outdone
6 outnumber

5.2 Serious gaming

VOCABULARY

A

1 alleged
2 acknowledge
3 asserted
4 implied
5 doubt
6 conclude

B

1 tap
2 nuts
3 coax
4 spur
5 inclined
6 act
7 steer

GRAMMAR

A

1 b 2 b 3 a 4 a 5 b 6 a 7 b 8 b

B

1 been reported (that)
2 is known
3 is understood to be
4 is believed to be
5 is rumored to be

C

1 The exam is understood to have been postponed.
2 Computer simulations are known to be extremely useful.
3 Our math professor is thought to be writing a book about Game Theory.
4 Everybody is expected to vote for the favorite.
5 The other player was alleged to have cheated.

5.3 Reading

READING

B

backgammon; conkers; video games; Clue

C

1 b 2 c 3 f 4 d 5 a 6 e

D

Possible answers

1 to illustrate the idea of how good it feels to win
2 teaching life skills such as cooperation and fair play
3 competency: the desire to feel in control/successfully deal with situations; desire for independence/making our own choices; relatedness: feeling important to others
4 competitiveness
5 'total absorption' – you are so focused you can't be distracted

5.4 Listening

LISTENING

B

1, 4, 5

C

1 b
2 a
3 a

5.5 Write a formal report

WRITING

A

Possible answers

1 Sports Unlimited
2 to investigate how games can improve motivation/efficiency in the workplace and recommend an app
3 GetFit

B

Possible answers

a Higher levels of motivation were observed in both staff and customers, … / Higher levels of motivation in both staff and customers were observed, …
b All activities (that are) performed by staff are recorded on an app on their smartphones and (then) turned into points.
c … it was decided that an investigation should be conducted …
d It should be mentioned, however, that an app such as the one used by *GetFit*, …
e Incentives for those doing work such as cleaning have also been introduced. / Incentives have also been introduced for those doing work such as cleaning.

1 c
2 b
3 a
4 e
5 d

WRITING PRACTICE

C

Model answer

Using games to attract customers to company exhibit space at the trade fair

Background

At a meeting of managerial staff to discuss the forthcoming trade fair in Venezuela, it was decided to investigate the effectiveness of using games in attracting more potential clients to the company's exhibit space. This report summarizes the research and offers some recommendations.

Traditional games

While they are still used by many companies at trade fairs to attract customers, traditional games are not regarded as being as interesting or exciting as digital games or virtual reality. However, they should not be rejected altogether. For example, a large container filled with tennis balls was used by one company as a guessing game, with a prize for the person who guessed the correct number of balls. People are still drawn to contests such as this.

Reality and virtual reality

Games and contests in which potential clients are invited to use our own sports equipment are another possibility (see recommendations). There might be some difficulty with regard to space, which is limited and expensive. Most people are attracted to virtual reality games, especially sports, and this would be a good way of promoting our products.

Recommendations

As golfing equipment is the company's best-selling range, it is recommended that efforts be concentrated on that. It would be easy to set up an indoor putting green and hold a contest with participants using the company's equipment. It is also recommended that a driving range simulator be installed – many business people are eager golfers. This might prove to be expensive but will undoubtedly attract additional visitors to the exhibit space. As far as traditional games are concerned, the idea of the container filled with tennis balls could be transformed into a large glass jar filled with own-brand golf balls, with an attractive prize for the winner. Customer numbers would significantly increase by putting these recommendations into practice.

6.1 Challenging journeys

VOCABULARY

A

1 uncharted
2 impenetrable
3 globetrotters
4 embarked
5 heart
6 provisions
7 long-haul
8 beaten

B

1 off
2 for
3 round
4 against
5 back
6 out
7 up
8 from

GRAMMAR

A

1 can't
2 might
3 likely
4 may have decided
5 have
6 possibility
7 must
8 may well

B

1 may well have
2 extremely probable/likely that
3 must have left
4 might have forgotten
5 a distinct possibility
6 can't have been

6.2 Inquisitive minds

GRAMMAR

A

1 reading
2 to spread
3 to maintain
4 to do
5 telling

B

1 c **2** d **3** e **4** a **5** b **6** f

C

1 b **2** a

VOCABULARY

A

1 quiet
2 By
3 take
4 greet
5 away
6 order
7 tidy
8 tear

B

1 and wide
2 to-riches
3 and soul
4 after time
5 to back
6 but surely
7 by side
8 or-/and-death

6.3 Reading

READING

C

1 Because of the success and recognition his trip to Sumatra had brought him
2 Being taken prisoner and lack of supplies (getting sick only happened after he had decided to turn back)
3 He was either very optimistic and determined or he wanted to hide his misfortunes.
4 They also disappeared.

6.4 Listening

LISTENING

B

Possible answers

1 (Robert Falcon) Scott and (Roald) Amundsen
2 to (be the first to) reach the South Pole
3 January 1912 and 1911: the speaker says that Amundsen reached the South Pole 34 days earlier
4 Amundsen reached the South Pole first; Scott and his men died on the return journey

C

Historical background
Goals
Route planning
Food and nutrition
Transportation

D

Possible answers

1 to map the area and study it
2 It was very hard – sickness, injury, hunger and cold.
3 tents, sleeping bags, building materials, food, fuel, bedding, clothing, scientific equipment
4 Scott – to study the area and to reach the South Pole; Amundsen – only to reach the South Pole
5 motor sleds, pony and dog sleds, man-hauling
6 the motor sleds didn't work, the ponies died, he didn't know how to handle the dogs
7 carefully, using flags and clearly marked food depots
8 he didn't allow enough calories per man; he didn't include any vitamins in the diet

6.5 Write an expository essay

WRITING

B

1 c 2 e 3 a 4 b 5 d

C

1 a 2 c 3 d 4 e 5 b

WRITING PRACTICE

C

Model answer

Travel broadens the mind, they say, and I believe this to be generally true. Some people are apprehensive about finding themselves in unfamiliar places, but life is supposed to be an adventure. Three of the many benefits of travel are learning about the world, reaching a better understanding of your own country and teaching you about yourself.

First, travel can teach you more about the world than any book, because you are experiencing the culture of another country first-hand. Engaging with the local people, you learn about their history and traditions, habits, food and even the way they think.

Second, it forces you to make comparisons – how your own culture differs from the one you are visiting. You will notice the cultural differences and see what makes your home country unique. In short, having traveled, you will see your own country with new eyes.

Finally, you can learn a lot about yourself by traveling. You will learn how you cope with unfamiliar situations, how you react to strange habits and customs. You will also learn about how much you are able to tolerate. Traveling will also test your language and social skills. You will return home a different person if you have fully immersed yourself in the experience of traveling.

In summary, traveling is a whole education in itself. The benefits gained from travel and experiencing other countries first-hand – greater knowledge of the world and how people do things differently (or the same), a new perspective on your own country and the self-knowledge gained – are immeasurable. In addition, you will have memories to treasure for a lifetime.

7.1 Beyond the limits

GRAMMAR

A

1 wasn't 2 that/which 3 it 4 it's 5 to 6 who/that 7 when 8 that/when

B

Possible answers

1 It was to raise money for charity that I applied to run the race.
2 It's the psychological not the physical challenge that's a problem for me!
3 It's only now that I've been running for five days that I've noticed the pain in my legs.
4 It was my sister who persuaded me to enter the race.
5 It wasn't a marathon that I ran – it was an ultramarathon!

C

Possible answers

1 It was the landscape paintings that they really wanted to see.
2 It was him who/that was to blame for breaking the window, not her.
3 It was the part at the end that Steven didn't understand.
4 It's you (that) I'm talking to!
5 It's the cost that bothers me.
6 It was because Eliza was scared that she said 'no'.
7 It's (only) when/after something's gone that you really appreciate it.
8 It was only when I got back that I realized how dangerous it was. / It wasn't until I got back that I realized how dangerous it was.

VOCABULARY

A

1 disgusted
2 resilient
3 superior
4 humble
5 devastated
6 courageous

B

1 courageous
2 humble
3 devastated
4 frustrated/grumpy
5 indifferent
6 superior
7 grumpy
8 hysterical

PRONUNCIATION

A

1 ↘ falling
2 ↗ rising
3 ↗ rising
4 ↘ falling
5 ↘ falling
6 ↗ rising

7.2 Extreme jobs

VOCABULARY

A

1 land 2 sick 3 competition 4 pressure 5 application 6 conditions

B

1 immensely
2 utterly
3 altogether
4 noticeably
5 relatively
6 remarkably
7 outright
8 radically
9 practically
10 somewhat

GRAMMAR

A

1 What ~~that~~ happened was I got confused.
2 Why ~~crashed~~ the computer **crashed** I have no idea!
3 Pets are easy – **all** they ~~all~~ need is food, water and some attention.
4 **What** ~~That~~ Lara likes about summer is being able to sleep on the balcony.
5 **All you** ~~You all~~ need is a snack and some good company.
6 **That's what** ~~What's that~~ Simon can't stand about this job – the silly rules!
7 **What** ~~That~~ we ended up doing was taking the train.
8 I didn't have my phone on me so what **I** did ~~I do~~ was ask a colleague to borrow hers.

B

1 What they did in the end was turn back.
2 All we need is a map.
3 What I can't stand is sleeping in a tent.
4 What Rex loves is playing with his ball in the yard.
5 All they needed was a drink of water.
6 What you need is a vacation.
7 What Tanya wanted more than anything was to be a ballerina.
8 All she's asking for is a short break.

C

1 What she loves most about
2 All (that) she wants is a
3 what he did was call
4 What I can't stand about/stand when
5 What I've realized is
6 All my sister remembers

PRONUNCIATION

A

1 The movie was really amazing, actually – we loved it!
2 I don't want any old doctor – I want the one I always see.
3 The questions they asked me were really ridiculous!
4 Any questions you have will be answered at the end, OK?
5 Well, you don't tell your password to just anybody.
6 Let's go – anywhere's better than here!
7 The test was really hard but he thinks he passed.
8 'Which movie do you want to watch?' 'Oh, any one. You choose.'

7.3 Reading

READING

B

Possible answers

1 drowning
2 It is the greatest sensual experience.
3 that it is a life spent traveling and having fun in exotic places
4 only if you are in the top rank and have sponsorships and endorsements

C

1 It
2 you
3 such incidents
4 Which
5 one
6 Many

7 that
8 those who
9 it's
10 that

D
1 surfing; C
2 the reader/people in general; E
3 shark attacks; A
4 dangers/riptides; A
5 a wave; A
6 surfers; E
7 surfing big waves/catching a wave as tall as a tower; A
8 non-surfers/onlookers; E
9 the lifestyle; A
10 prize money; A

7.4 Listening

LISTENING

B
1 circus
2 1978
3 16 million
4 documentary
5 New York
6 40
7 in secret
8 bow and arrow

C
1 b
2 c
3 c
4 a

7.5 Write a cover letter

WRITING

B
2 climbing ability; skill in the use and maintenance of power tools; working at height; calmness in tense situations; ability to follow instructions and to work well with others

C
Possible answers
1 led/managed
2 tasked with collecting
3 managed
4 oversaw/coordinated/organized
5 I (also) developed

WRITING PRACTICE

C
Model answer
Dear Mr. Scholes,

I am writing to apply for the position of Lifeguard Team Leader at Ocean Resorts.

You will see from my résumé (attached) that I have four years' experience as a beach lifeguard in Australia, where I headed up a team of 20 lifeguards and coordinated sea and air rescue services when necessary. I have rescued swimmers from shark attacks on several occasions, so am able to work under pressure. During that time, I trained as a paramedic and have a good knowledge of first aid.

I have a lifesaving certification from Australia and since coming to this country have acquired an RLSS certification. In fact, I achieved the highest grade of my intake. I have worked poolside at a spa here for three years, and my duties included liaising with customer care and sometimes helping with front-of-house duties. Although I am no longer part of the Australian 4x4 medley relay team, I have kept up my training regimen and remain as strong a swimmer as ever.
I look forward to your response.

Best regards,
Bruce MacNamara

8.1 Health and wellness

VOCABULARY

A
1 sore
2 rash
3 rate
4 pressure
5 sprained
6 fractured
7 pulled
8 dislocate

B
1 fractured
2 pulled
3 inflamed
4 rate
5 sore
6 sprained
7 rash
8 blood

GRAMMAR

A
1 into
2 in
3 to
4 To/With
5 with/in
6 to
7 of/about
8 among/of

B
1 the person whose fitness business is now worth millions
2 the person (who) I trust more than anyone
3 whereby it is impossible for me to get a virus
4 a training injury from which you might never recover
5 people for whom exercise is not a priority
6 into whose pockets the profits all go, is very satisfied

8.2 Sports and wellness

VOCABULARY

A

1 gut feeling
2 gave him food for thought
3 got cold feet
4 give it his best shot
5 out of his depth
6 throwing in the towel

B

1 fizzy
2 Crunchy/Crisp
3 sour
4 mild
5 appetizing
6 creamy/cheesy
7 tangy; acidic
8 bland
9 soggy

PRONUNCIATION

A

1 isn't really my cup of tea
2 made a meal of it
3 keep an eye out
4 with a grain of salt
5 head and shoulders above
6 moving the goalposts

GRAMMAR

A

1 more
2 either
3 Most people
4 some
5 others
6 very few
7 of
8 little

B

1 When you're doing a serious hike, you can't drink too much ~~of~~ water – in fact, most people don't drink enough.
2 There were two vegan options, but I didn't want **either** ~~both~~ of them.
3 **Those** ~~They~~ who followed the diet reported an average loss of three kilos in the first week.
4 You have too much sugar and salt in your diet – it's best if you cut back on **both** ~~neither~~.
5 There are only **a** / ~~only~~ **very** few restaurants that serve good vegetarian food in this city.
6 You drink a lot of coffee, and I think you'd sleep better if you drank less ~~of~~.
7 These are your books – **mine** ~~my~~ are still over there where I left them.
8 Jamie only needs six hours of sleep a night, but I can never seem to get enough ~~of~~.

8.3 Reading

READING

A

Charcoal – c
Ketogenic – a
Cauliflower – d
Vegan – b

B

1 the keto diet
2 the vegan diet
3 the charcoal diet

C

Possible answers

1 Interestingly; Admittedly
2 supposedly; allegedly
3 positive attitude: There's no doubt
neutral attitude: It is also thought to
skeptical attitude: it seems
4 colloquial asides: I don't know about you
tag questions: Sounds rather scientific, doesn't it?
rhetorical questions: Black cheese … anyone?

8.4 Listening

LISTENING

C

1 b **2** a **3** a **4** a

D

1 right amount of calories; vitamins; nutrients; vitamin D; supplements
2 bone fractures
3 resistance training
4 excessive
5 duck breast; capers; lobster; chocolate cake

8.5 Write a summary

WRITING

B

Possible answers

1 'overtraining syndrome'; symptoms; physiological; psychological
2 Summary a misses the point and is irrelevant.
Summary b is the best because it includes the key points, phrased clearly in the writer's own words and without changing the original meaning.
Summary c repeats language from the text almost word for word.

C

Possible answers

1 increased heart rate; weight loss; excessive thirst
2 the negative physical effects of overtraining
3 The physical symptoms of overtraining to look out for are loss of both weight and muscle, inability to put on muscle and constant thirst. Further symptoms include an increase in heart rate, fluctuations in blood pressure, injury and susceptibility to infections.

WRITING PRACTICE

C

Model answer

Physical symptoms of overtraining syndrome include loss of both weight and muscle, inability to put on muscle and constant thirst. Psychological symptoms include a lack of readiness for training, sleeping problems and tiredness, changes in mood and a loss of confidence. Overtraining syndrome can be treated by identifying symptoms, seeking medical help and adopting a varied training regime with periods of rest.

9.1 Language and behavior

VOCABULARY

A

1 stoked
2 whining
3 bloke; dude
4 shady; stolen
5 TV; like; wheels

B

1 shambles 2 crashed 3 could do with 4 set her back 5 grand 6 bucks 7 broke 8 in good shape

PRONUNCIATION

A

1 I feel kind of strange – like I've been here before or something.
2 We have to give a talk, or a speech, or something like that.
3 I have to do some jobs – shopping, cleaning and so on.
4 You know, I think that, in some way or another, he must be involved.
5 So, in a sense, this is the easiest job in the world!
6 What do you take me for – some sort of fool?
7 Don't give me excuses like you overslept or whatever.
8 My course covers health and safety issues, stuff like that.

GRAMMAR

A

1 Those students who haven't completed the assignment should stay behind at the end of the lecture.
2 Both of the solutions he suggested sounded a little like a desperate attempt to please the boss.
3 He invested all the money he'd saved up into some crazy get-rich-quick scheme and lost everything.
4 The thing that annoys Pierre most is the way young people don't seem to care about language.
5 Three of the 20 people present were first-time attendees.
6 The idea that simply punishing children teaches them to behave has fallen out of favor with many modern educationalists.
7 Do you know a good place to eat that would suit a group of hungry teenagers?
8 Sometimes it seems to me that almost everyone I know is hooked on some computer game or other.

B

1 I spend **almost** all my free time ~~almost~~ doing sports.
2 The belief **that** ~~what~~ you can change things is all you need in order to make a difference.
3 The person (**who/that**) ~~where~~ I spoke to didn't seem to have a clue what was happening.
4 I need a place **to stay** ~~for staying~~ for a few days.
5 Both ~~of~~ / of **the** ideas seem a little hard to put into practice.
6 The woman ~~who~~ / who **is** sitting next to Claire is Frances.
7 Very few ~~of~~ / of **the** people in this country have traveled abroad.
8 The interviewer was impressed by the fact (**that**) ~~how~~ I knew so much about their company.

C

1 most
2 The / That
3 one
4 of
5 their
6 that

9.2 Animal behavior

VOCABULARY

A

1 c 2 f 3 h 4 b 5 g 6 d 7 a 8 e

B

1 gazing 2 fidgeting 3 shrugged 4 shook 5 blinked 6 beckoned 7 pointed 8 raised

GRAMMAR

A

1 Having got/woken up early
2 Despite not knowing
3 Done properly, the job
4 Not being practical, reading the
5 Having just bought a new
6 Given the right

B

1 ~~They were feeling~~ (**Feeling**) threatened, the animals instinctively hid behind the wall.
2 **Having** ~~Had~~ never / **Never having** ~~never~~ been on a plane before, I was both excited and nervous.
3 If ~~you~~ / you **are** successful in your application, you will be notified by email.
4 **Having grown** ~~Grown~~ up in the US, Marvin has always spoken English well.
5 ~~Been~~ (**Being**) exhausted and short on money, Carrie cut short her trip to Bolivia.
6 Before **starting** ~~started~~ work in insurance, Lionel was a factory worker.
7 Despite **not/never having** ~~I hadn't~~ been there before, I soon found my way around.
8 While suffering badly from the flu, **Angela was visited by** a couple of close friends ~~visited Angela~~ every day.

C

1 b 2 c 3 c 4 b 5 a 6 b

9.3 Reading

READING

C

1 T
2 F (They were told this, but the experiment was to see if their behavior was influenced by the words they had processed.)
3 F (They were timed from the moment they finished the task to see how quickly they interrupted, if at all.)
4 T
5 F (The opposite appears to be true – we make major life choices based on similarities of the names of people and things to our own name.)

D

Possible answers

1 to see how long the students would wait before interrupting and to see if students who had been exposed to the 'rude' words interrupted sooner
2 As predicted, students who had been given the 'rude' words interrupted sooner than the others.
3 Bargh himself was reluctant to conclude that exposure to certain types of words makes us behave in that way (because it was a very small sample).

9.4 Listening

LISTENING

C

1 F ('I've lived here for … four years.')
2 T
3 F (Rob says, 'I'd be bummed if I didn't get the grades I want to go to college. … there is a reason behind the pressure.')
4 T
5 T
6 F (The Steiner school has a *'holistic' approach to learning* and doesn't divide it into specific subject areas.)

D

3 I've lived here for … [~~let~~ me see] … ~~for~~ four years.
4 ~~Be~~cause it's [~~you~~ know] … it's really *unique* [~~and~~ stuff].
5 Is it [one ~~of~~] those places where ~~you~~ can, [~~you~~ know], do anything you want?

9.5 Write a conclusion to an academic report

WRITING

B

a 3 **b** 2 **c** 1 **d** 4

C

1 c **2** b **3** e **4** a/d **5** d/a

D

Colon (Students underline any two of the following)
'… individual responsibility is ignored: normal values and the ability to reason are abandoned.'
'… convergence theorists argue that individuals in a crowd do not lose personal identity: personal beliefs and values are communicated …'
'… our research revealed that … in a crowd: crowd catalysts such as police presence …'

Semi-colon
'… most of the research so far stems from disciplines such as psychology and sociology; there has been little recent research into crowd behavior at large outdoor events.'
'They fail to demonstrate why some crowds … behave differently; nor do they examine the difference between …'

WRITING PRACTICE

C

Model answer

Our research attempted to answer the questions of whether the use of slang had increased among the general population in recent years. This proved difficult at first; there is no reliable source of data on the frequency of the use of slang words from before 1970 with which to compare our findings. Nonetheless, we are confident our results relatively accurately reflect the current situation.

There is no doubt that we have been exposed to more informal language and slang since the introduction of the internet and social media, on television and in movies, too. However, our research shows that this is not reflected in the workplace: the average person is not using or exposed to slang more frequently in his/her professional life. In our most recent survey, a larger proportion of the subjects were women; previous surveys were heavily weighted in favor of men. It is clear from the results that women today on average use slang as much as, but not more than, men.

Our research also found that the most frequently used slang expressions have remained much the same for the past 20 years, with newer terms and expressions not yet replacing the older words and phrases in popularity. We suggest that such data be collected periodically to see how the use of individual slang terms changes over time.

In conclusion, our data do not show that the use of slang has increased.

10.1 Urban problems

VOCABULARY

A

1 designated
2 habitats; endangered
3 architectural; heritage
4 ruins; settlement
5 preserve; funds; refurbish

B

1 urge **2** desire **3** responsibility **4** obligation **5** failure **6** refusal **7** tendency **8** reminder

PRONUNCIATION

B

1 up
2 down
3 down
4 up
5 down
6 down
7 up
8 up

GRAMMAR

A

1 h **2** c **3** i **4** b **5** j **6** a **7** g **8** f **9** e **10** d

B

1 despite it being
2 any case, I have
3 namely Australia and China
4 owing to the bad weather
5 whereas the return journey seemed
6 As a matter of fact

10.2 How to change the world

VOCABULARY

A

1 b **2** a **3** c **4** c **5** a **6** c **7** b **8** c

B

1 passionate
2 effective
3 personal
4 persuasive
5 apathetic
6 community

GRAMMAR

A

1 Some people think we can change the world but I don't ~~think we can change the world~~.
2 If you get the opportunity to go, you should ~~take the opportunity to go~~.
3 A lot of people struggle with course fees and I wish they didn't ~~struggle with course fees~~.
4 They should target governments and ~~they should target~~ large companies.
5 We're going to have food and ~~we're going to have~~ music.
6 You asked me if I thought we could make a difference and the answer is yes ~~I do think we can make a difference~~.
7 I know a lot of people who are pessimistic about the future, but I'm not ~~pessimistic about the future~~.
8 ~~Are~~ you joining us for pizza? ~~Do you have~~ any preference ~~as to what we order~~?

B

1 do it / do so
2 he does
3 I do
4 do that/it
5 so
6 do so/that
7 hope not
8 do that

10.3 Reading

READING

A

traffic congestion and the related problem of air pollution

B

Possible answers

	Problems	Solutions	Criticism
UK	Health problems	Workplace parking fee improve public transportation, electric cars	Job losses, strain on public transportation
Paris	Premature deaths	Anti-pollution stickers, fines if no sticker, car manufacturers make non-polluting cars	Few people buy the stickers, people taxed off the road
Freiburg		Pedestrianized city center, cheap and efficient public transportation, prioritize walking, biking and public transportation, incentives for people who don't use cars, good urban planning	

10.4 Listening

LISTENING

B

Possible answers

1 a job interview
2 living in an isolated place
3 the job

C

1 environmental science
2 East
3 two
4 (natural) habitats
5 deer
6 paths
7 preserve
8 endangering
9 research

D

1 When speaking to Dr. Ramsey, Jonathan says 'Hello Dr. Ramsey. How do you do?'
2 When speaking to Dr. Ramsey, Jonathan says 'A glass of water would be great, thank you.'
3 When speaking to Dr. Ramsey, Jonathan says 'I have a degree in environmental science from the University of East Anglia and actually have practical experience from several field trips.'
4 When speaking to Dr. Ramsey, Jonathan says 'I really feel that the job is an ideal opportunity for me and it involves everything that I enjoy doing.'

10.5 Write a persuasive essay

WRITING

B

Possible answers

1 Tourism has a largely negative impact.
2 environmental damage; disrespect for local cultures, traditions and behaviors; lack of benefit for local workers and business
3 Yes. Understanding different cultures; money and job creation

C

1 Paragraph 4
2 Counter-argument: that mass tourism brings economic benefits – more money and more jobs. Rebuttal: the jobs are seasonal, low-skilled and insecure; most of the money goes to large foreign companies, not the local economy.
Yes, the rebuttal directly answers the counter-argument.
3 Counter-argument: 'There is an argument that …'
Rebuttal: 'While this is true up to a point, …'

WRITING PRACTICE

C

Model answer

More and more shopping malls are being built in or near towns and cities all over the world. While some argue that they provide a more convenient and fun shopping 'experience', I would argue that they create a negative impact on local communities which outweighs their convenience.
Perhaps the greatest negative impact of shopping malls is felt by local businesses who, being unable to compete, can lose up to 90% of their business. The community as a whole loses out, because local businesses play an important role in creating community identity.

Shopping malls also have a huge carbon footprint; shopping centers in the US are estimated to create 12 million tons of waste each year, including packaging and food waste. They also waste energy through excessive lighting, day and night, and heat loss through constantly opening doors.

Supporters of shopping mall developments claim that people benefit from the lower prices at malls, somewhere to park, the convenience of being able to do all their shopping under one roof and the fact that malls also provide all kinds of recreational activities, turning shopping into a fun day out for all the family. Yet the concentration of so much in one place brings its own problems, such as increased traffic, pollution, overcrowding and noise.

In summary, the negative effects of shopping malls on local communities outweigh any advantages. They destroy local businesses and community identity, create an enormous amount of waste and have a negative impact on the environment. These are all reasons enough, I believe, to encourage people to shop locally.